# CYCADS
# OF
# SOUTH
# AFRICA

# CYCADS OF SOUTH AFRICA

CYNTHIA GIDDY

with pencil drawings and diagrams
by Barbara Jeppe

PURNELL

CAPE TOWN   JOHANNESBURG   LONDON   NEW YORK

PUBLISHED BY PURNELL AND SONS (S.A.) (PTY) LTD.
70 KEEROM STREET, CAPE TOWN

SBN 360 00274 9

Second Impression 1978.

Set in 12/14 pt Bembo by Sparham & Ford Cape (Pty) Ltd., Cape Town
Colour reproduction by Hirt and Carter (Pty) Ltd., Cape Town
Printed and bound by ABC Press (Pty) Ltd., Cape Town

# Acknowledgements

It would not have been possible to write this book without the help, enthusiasm and generosity of so many people. Much of the enjoyment I have had in writing this book has been in sharing the project with fellow enthusiasts and friends.

I would like to thank Barbara Jeppe for her sustained interest, encouragement and generous help. Her diagrams, leaf sketches and drawings have added immeasurably to the text and I am most grateful.

I am indebted beyond mere words to:

Bruce Bursey who showed me the cycads of the Eastern Cape and whom I would like to commend for his pioneer work in hand pollinating and raising cycads from seed.

André Liebenberg whose wide knowledge of the flora and ecology of Zululand made my task so much easier.

Henry Richards who taught a layman how to identify cycads and who located so many of the plants in cone for me to photograph.

I would like to thank the many cycad growers and enthusiasts who so readily gave valuable information on growth patterns in cultivation and allowed me to photograph plants in their gardens. They are:

Mr and Mrs J. Ansley, Mr Anthony Bannister, Adv H. A. de Ridder, Mr and Mrs Jaap de Villiers, Prof J. F. Eloff, Mrs J. J. Fraser, Mr Tino Ferero, Mr Ray Ferguson, Mr W. J. Geringer, Mrs. J. P. Gebbert, Mrs Sally Geldenhuys, Mr J. O. Heyns, Dr Albert Hertzog, Mr Jimmie Hall, Mr David Hardy, the late Mr Bill Henstock, Dr and Mrs A. J. Jonker, Mr and Mrs Boet Lombaard, Mr Hex Modjadji, Mr G. Myers, Mr Johan Meintjies, Mr Louis Naude, Mr Ben Naude, Mr Hennie Naude, Mr P. C. Oberholzer, Mr G. Prinsloo, Mr and Mrs C. T. Phillips, Mrs M. Pierneef, Mr Pierre Pienaar, Mr Emdin Pienaar, Mr and Mrs Victor Pringle, Mr A. Prozesky, Mr and Mrs Dan Roux, Mr Denis Stevenson, Mr Robert Southey, Miss Ailsa Tecklenberg, Mr and Mrs Dan Timm, Mr D. P. van Heerden, Mr F. A. van der Merwe, Mr and Mrs Jannie Venter, Mr M. van Biljon, Dr J. L. Viljoen, Mrs Emily Vosloo, Mr P. Welken.

I received every assistance and help from:

Prof Brian Rycroft and the staff at Kirstenbosch in Cape Town.

Mr Ernest Thorp and the staff at the Durban Botanic Gardens.

Mr Peter Law and the staff at the Pietermaritzburg Botanic Gardens.

Dr R. A. Dyer and the staff of the National Botanical Research Institute in Pretoria.

Dr Courtney-Latimer of the East London Museum. I do thank them for giving so generously of their time, knowledge and experience.

Mrs Esme Hennessy of the Department of Botany at the University of Durban-Westville made many constructive suggestions and clarified many points on botany.

Prof P. J. Robbertse and Miss Suzelle Ferreira of the Department of Botany at the University of Pretoria read parts of the manuscript and I am indebted to them for helpful advice.

I would like to thank the staff of the Transvaal Museum in Pretoria for technical assistance in the identification of the insect pests.

During the past three years Messrs Spectrum Photo Finishers of Durban gave the most careful and individual attention to my transparencies and I thank them. The photographs are all my own with the exception of the picture of the male cone of *E. ghellinckii*. I am grateful to Miss Lorna Peirson for the loan of this slide taken on a mountaineering outing to this almost inaccessible habitat.

Gail Lyons spent many hours typing and retyping the manuscript and I am most grateful.

For their hospitality and friendship during my frequent visits I would like to thank Joan Bursey, Marieta Ferero, Marina Liebenberg and Koekie Richards.

Finally, I would like to thank my husband Ted for his support and love when the project sometimes seemed too ambitious and my daughters Caitlin, Janet, Louise and Laurel who so cheerfully assumed the household duties during my frequent and prolonged absences from home.

# *Preface*

It has been my privilege to stand in the swirl of cloud and mist among the age-old stems of the Modjadji Palms on the hill below the Kraal of the Rain Queen and feel something of the magic of rain in Africa.

In the Karoo among the bush and scrub, I marvelled at the fresh blue-green leaves of *E. lehmannii* in the searing summer sun on a day when even the euphorbias looked wilted.

In Zululand I realised the infinite pains Nature takes to ensure her survival. On the eastern shores of Lake Sibaya a clump of *E. ferox* grows under every Umdoni tree, here and there and further away. Then, when the eerie cry of the Trumpeter Hornbill is heard, the pattern falls into place. With the bright red, fleshy seed firmly clasped in his beak, he flies off, swallows it and some nights later while roosting in an Umdoni tree, the kernel now devoid of flesh, is regurgitated. Nature in the shade and damp and humus below, receives, succours and nurtures the seedling and so completes the cycle.

Cycads have a majesty and grandeur unmatched in the wild places and it is with a measure of sadness that one sees one of these giants standing in a small suburban garden amidst the clutter of civilization.

Only when Man realises that he too is of the earth and not merely on it, will he regain the immortality of his spirit.

The cycads do not belong to us. They were here before us. They belong to the generations not yet born.

# References

For many years Dr R. A. Dyer and Dr Inez Verdoorn have worked on the genera of *Encephalartos* and *Stangeria*. In various scientific journals notably *The Journal of South African Botany*, *The Flora of Southern Africa Vol. I* and *Bothalia Vol. VIII part 4*, they have classified and described many species and I have continuously referred to and been guided by their work while compiling this book.

I have found *Trees of Southern Africa* by Eve Palmer and Norah Pitman of great interest.

The various contributions on cycads in the Rhodesian Aloe, Succulent and Cactus Society's Journal *Excelsa* have been most helpful.

For the section on the toxicity of cycads I consulted *The Medicinal and Poisonous Plants of Southern and Eastern Africa* by J. M. Watt and M. G. Breyer-Brandwijk. *The Morphology of Gymnosperms* by K. D. Sporne and *A Glossary of Botanic Terms* by B. Daydon Jackson were invaluable.

*The Living Cycads* by C. J. Chamberlain published in 1919 made absorbing reading and is historically of interest in describing cycad localities which no longer exist.

# Foreword

by
PROFESSOR H. BRIAN RYCROFT,
M.Sc., B.Sc. (For.), Ph.D., F.L.S., F.R.S.S.Af., F.R.H.S.,
Hon. F. Inst. P.A. (S.A.)
Director, National Botanic Gardens of South Africa, Kirstenbosch
Harold Pearson  Professor of Botany at the University of Cape Town.

Cycads have intrigued botanists for many years. Perhaps because they do not bear flowers, these plants have escaped the attention of gardeners until fairly recently. Along with Aloes, Proteas, Ericas and various other indigenous shrubs and trees, Cycad plants have become the pride and joy of many a city or farm garden.

Apart from monographs, no non-technical but scientifically accurate information on Cycads has been available to the public. Cynthia Giddy spent three years researching Cycads of South Africa. She consulted many professional botanists as well as amateur growers. From a wealth of information gleaned, she has written a concise factual book not only to provide gardeners with much useful cultural information but a reference work for botanists and students.

Above all, the excellent colour photographs used to illustrate the book will prove invaluable in aiding all concerned in identifying the various Cycad species. The habitat photographs are a notable contribution, since many garden-grown specimens do not remain true to type. In addition, illustrations include leaf details of each species as well as a complete set of male and female cones. The cone photographs are no mean feat either, as many South African Cycads produce cones very irregularly.

In keeping with an awareness for the urgent need to conserve indigenous flora, a very strong plea for the conservation of these plants has been made. Readers are well informed on the best methods of growing Cycads from seed, which is the final answer, since many species are no longer able to regenerate in their natural habitats. One hopes that in creating an awareness of the value of Cycads, this book may also prevent the needless destruction of these very slow-growing plants by otherwise ignorant homeowners, farmers and others.

It is my very great pleasure to recommend this excellent publication to readers, in the knowledge that anyone interested in Cycads will find much information, both for profit and for pleasure.

# Contents

# List of Diagrams

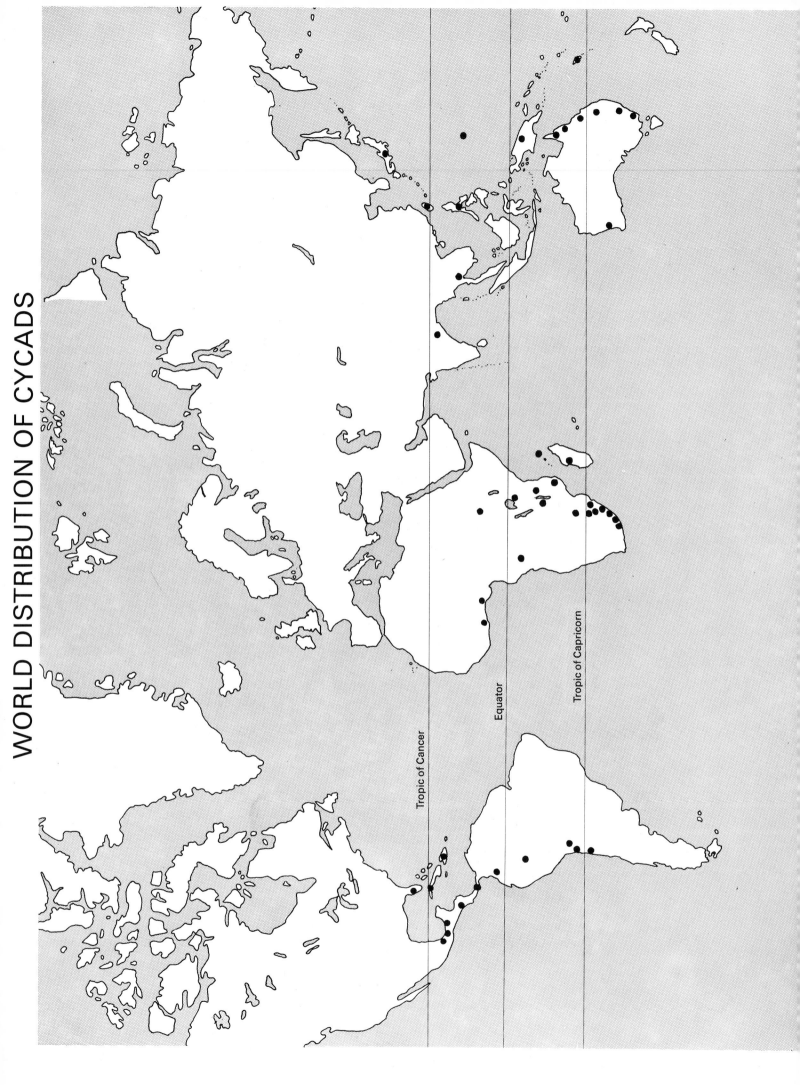

WORLD DISTRIBUTION OF CYCADS

Tropic of Cancer

Equator

Tropic of Capricorn

# Introduction

Cycads are the most primitive living seedbearing plants known and belong to an ancient order, the Cycadales which flourished in the Carboniferous period 50 to 60 million years ago. This was the period when the vast coal beds were formed and the earth enjoyed a warm and humid climate. The cycads we know today have changed little in their basic character and could well be described as the Coelacanths of the plant world.

At the present time only 10 genera belonging to 3 families survive and total about 150 species distributed throughout the tropical and temperate regions of the world. In the past all living cycads were thought to belong to one family. In 1959 L. A. S. Johnson in the 'Proceedings of the Linnaean Society of New South Wales' restricted the family Cycadaceae to the single genus *Cycas*, he created the family Stangeriaceae for the monotypic South African genus *Stangeria* and resuscitated the family Zamiaceae for all the remaining genera *Zamia, Dioon, Ceratozamia, Microcycas, Macrozamia, Lepidozamia, Bowenia* and *Encephalartos.*

Cycads, a term which will be used for the South African genera of *Encephalartos* and *Stangeria*, are often confused with both palms and tree ferns because of a superficial resemblance. Botanically these three plants are totally unrelated.

Cycads belong to the group of plants called Gymnosperms i.e. plants which bear naked seeds. The reproductive organs are produced in cones which are different from the typical flower of the Angiosperms. The seeds of Gymnosperms are not enclosed in an ovary and no stigma or style is present. The Gymnosperms are conebearing plants and are represented in South Africa by the Cycads (28 species of *Encephalartos* and 1 species of *Stangeria*) the Yellowwoods (4 species of *Podocarpus*) the Cedars (3 species of *Widdringtonia*) and the monotypic genus *Welwitschia bainesii.*

## Distribution of Cycads

Cycads occur in the tropical and the temperate regions of both hemispheres in Central America, Africa, Asia and Australia.

They are distributed as follows:

FAMILY     CYCADACEAE

Genus         *Cycas*

                  Japan, India, Thailand, Formosa, Philipines, Okinawa, New Caledonia, New Guinea, Australia, The Comoro Islands, Madagascar, East Coast of Africa, Mozambique

| FAMILY | ZAMIACEAE |
|--------|-----------|
| Genus  | *Bowenia* |
|        | Australia |
| Genus  | *Lepidozamia* |
|        | Australia |
| Genus  | *Macrozamia* |
|        | Australia |
| Genus  | *Microcycas* |
|        | Cuba |
| Genus  | *Dioon* |
|        | Mexico |
| Genus  | *Ceratozamia* |
|        | Mexico |
| Genus  | *Zamia* |
|        | Florida U.S.A., Mexico, Columbia, Dominican Republic, Cuba, Costa Rica, Puerto Rico, West Indies, Cayman Isles, Brazil, Bolivia, Chile |
| Genus  | *Encephalartos* |
|        | South Africa, Rhodesia, Mozambique, Tanzania, Uganda, Ghana, Malawi, Kenya, Zaire, Sudan, Nigeria |
| FAMILY | STANGERIACEAE |
| Genus  | *Stangeria* |
|        | South Africa |

Looking at the world map (page 12) and noting the distribution of cycads in each region, the pattern is obvious. On every continent they are found today only in those regions where climatic conditions are most favourable. The tropical and temperate zones.

The cycads have persisted to the present day but only as remnants of a great range of forms which 150 million years ago had an almost world-wide distribution.

# *Echoes of the past and a view of the future*

The recorded history of South African botany probably began when an unknown Dutch sailor took back to Europe a specimen of *Protea neriifolia*. This was the first South African plant to be illustrated and it appeared in a book by Clusius published in Antwerp in 1605. After the Dutch settlement at the Cape in 1652, a steady stream of plants began to flow to Europe and in turn, many botanists and explorers came to the Cape to collect and record at first hand our floral wealth. The earliest plants described were those in the immediate vicinity of the Cape but as the hinterland was opened up, more and more species were added to the growing number of South African plants studied, illustrated and grown in Europe.

The first cycad was collected by Carl Peter Thunberg, one of the most distinguished of the early travellers who is often referred to as 'the father of South African botany'. Thunberg came to South Africa in 1772 and during his stay of just less than three years collected more than 3 000 specimens. He travelled extensively from Cape Town northwards to the Olifants River and eastwards to the Sundays River. It was on the latter expedition accompanied by Francis Masson from Kew Gardens that Thunberg came upon his Breadtree. His account of the plant, its occurrence and its uses is full of interest:

'The Bread tree Zamia caffra is a species of palm, which grows on the
> hills, below the mountains, on these tracts. It was of the height and thickness of a man at most, very much spread, and single. I have sometimes seen from one root, two or three stems spring. It is out of the pith (medulla) of this tree that the Hottentots contrive to prepare their bread. For this purpose, after scooping out the pith, they bury it in the earth and leave it there for a space of two months to rot, after which they knead it, and make it into a cake which they slightly bake in the embers. I observed that the tree stood in dry sterile places and grew slowly.'

This was the plant known today as *Encephalartos longifolius*.

When one reads the journals of these early botanical travellers one marvels at their indifference to the dangers and difficulties encountered on the way, ranging from wild animals and hostile tribes to the total absence of all trails in an unknown territory. Thunberg however did not have to cope with petrol restrictions and odd customs hours at the Swaziland border post.

The introduction of living plants to Europe from South Africa in the eighteenth and nineteenth century was no mean task. Discovering a new species was often the easiest part, the plant then had to be transported uninjured from its habitat to a port where it could be held and cared for until a ship called. The long sea voyage to Europe was an added risk with fresh water on board being in short supply for drinking purposes let alone horticultural uses. The plant of *Encephalartos longifolius* which Francis Masson collected with Thunberg in 1772 is still flourishing at Kew more than two hundred years later.

By the end of the nineteenth century more than half the species known today had been discovered and described. One of the most singular discoveries being that of *E. woodii*. In 1895 Medley Wood, then Director of the Natal Government Herbarium found a single male plant, consisting of four large stems and some offshoots in the Ngoye forest in Zululand. In 1903 Medley Wood sent John Wylie to collect some specimens for cultivation. Three of the smaller offshoots were planted in the Durban Botanic Gardens and other specimens were sent to Kew and to Messrs Sander and Co. of St. Albans in England. Sander writing in the Gardeners Chronicle in 1908 described his plant as *E. woodii*, previously it had been known as *E. altensteinii* var. *bispinosa*. In 1907 Wylie returned to Ngoye and brought back two of the larger trunks which were also planted in the Durban Botanic Gardens and may still be seen on either side of the steps leading up to the old Conservatory. The last two stems were collected in 1916 on instructions from Wylie. One was sent to the Division of Botany in Pretoria and the other was planted in the garden of Mr Maurice Evans who with Medley Wood produced the first illustrated botanical book produced entirely in South Africa. Several expeditions since then have failed to produce another specimen of *E. woodii* and a female plant is not known. All the specimens in cultivation are suckers from the original plant. *E. woodii* is considered by many to be one of the rarest plants in the world.

A discovery no less thrilling was that made by Dr Inez Verdoorn when in 1944 she rediscovered and identified *E. eugene-maraisii*. The story begins in 1926 when her uncle, the poet and naturalist, Eugene Marais found a cycad in the Waterberg area of the Transvaal and sent it to Dr Rudolf Marloth in Cape Town for identification. Children who had eaten the seed had become ill and Eugene Marais had treated them. Marloth could not believe that it had been found at that locality, because until then all the cycads had been found in the eastern part of the country. Some years later Eugene Marais while visiting his niece remarked upon the cycad he had collected in the Waterberg. Inez Verdoorn checked the original specimen sent to Marloth and plied him with questions but before Eugene Marais could take her to show her the locality, he too died. But her interest in this new species did not die and finally in 1944, Inez Verdoorn with the help of an extension officer P. S. Toerien located *E. eugene-maraisii* very close to the locality where Eugene Marais had found it eighteen years previously.

It is difficult to believe that a plant as large and remarkable as a cycad can be overlooked, but further new species followed; *E. inopinus* in 1955, *E. cupidus* and *E. heenanii* in 1969 and at the present time at least another three are being investigated.

Since the time of Thunberg and Masson, cycads have fired the imagination of botanists and gardeners alike. These decorative plants that are imbued with an almost mystical antiquity have had their numbers severely depleted to adorn private and public gardens throughout the world. Records show that many thousands were exported abroad during the last century. From the register kept by McKen, Curator of the Durban Botanic Gardens we learn that in one year alone from April 1866 to April 1867 no less than 238 cycads were sent to England, Belgium, Prussia, Ceylon and Mauritius.

The figures are however puny compared with our own local raids on the veld. As much as one encourages the use of indigenous plants in home gardens, it should not be at the expense of the species in its habitat. In the last decade the cycad has become a "status" plant to be acquired at all costs regardless of the ultimate cost. Plants that may be a hundred years old or more are ruthlessly uprooted and replanted in an alien climate. Unaware and ignorant of their growth cycles, plants that do not push out leaves within a few months are abandoned and land on the refuse heap.

So serious was the situation that the Transvaal declared all cycads Specially Protected Plants in 1971 and required that all those who had cycads in their possession apply for a permit. Within 18 months more than 8 000 permits for more than 64 000 cycads had been issued. One wonders whether there are perhaps not more cycads in city gardens (where they seldom reproduce) than there are left in Nature? And, if 64 000 survived, how many died in transplanting?

Cycads are protected not only in the Transvaal but in all the Provinces and strict protective laws and heavy penalties are laid down by the Nature Conservation Ordinances of each province.

What of the future?

Cycads have survived for over 50 million years with little change in their basic character. Neither fire nor drought presents any real danger to the survival of the species, only Man.

Where plants are threatened with actual destruction in the form of roadbuilding, dams or township development, removal from the habitat is justified and it is fitting to record that when the J. G. Strijdom dam was built on the Pongola River 6 000 plants of *E. lebomboensis* were rescued by Operation Wildflower.

Many thousands of mature cycads produce cones every year in cultivation. Few collectors have both a male and female plant of the same species that cone at the same time. I would like to see the formation of a Pollen Bank where deepfrozen pollen can be stored and enthusiasts by hand-pollination could cut down on the wastage of potentially fertile seed. In nature a single cone of *E. altensteinii* produces over 500 fertile seeds. Very few seedlings survive in the veld. Conservation bodies should make fertile seed available to both home gardeners and commercial nurseries and encourage them to artificially propagate the most endangered species so that the pressure may be removed from the natural supplies. By growing cycads from seed we can live on the interest while keeping the capital intact.

# MORPHOLOGY OF CYCADS

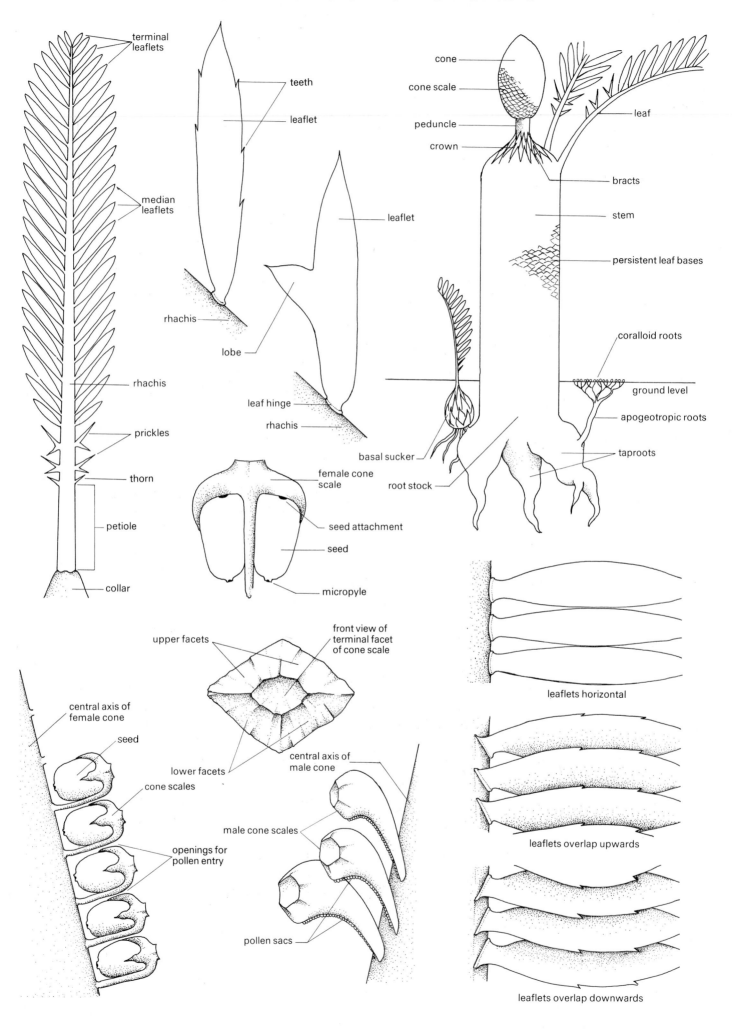

# General characteristics

*Vegetative structures and their functions*

*Stem*

Cycads are often mistaken for palms because the unbranched stem and crown of leaves resemble a palm tree. In fact, the word cycad is derived from the Greek word 'cyckos' meaning 'palmlike'. The stems may be either subterranean or reach a height of 10 m or more. They are usually un-branched. When branching occurs in the columnar types, it is usually the result of an injury to the stem. Many species also sucker from the base. Species such as *Encephalartos humilis, E. horridus, E. trispinosus, E. cycadifolius* and *E. cupidus* frequently form clusters of 10 to 12 plants. The columnar species are usually single stemmed while the stem is upright. When it begins to lean with age and the weight of the leafcrown, suckers form from the base.

Externally the stem consists of a thick layer of persistent leafbases. These leafbases become very compressed lower down as the weight of the stem increases and they cannot be clearly distinguished in species such as *E. woodii*. A transverse section of the stem (Colour Plate A, fig. 6) shows the outer layer of leafbases which are spirally arranged. The large pith in the centre is surrounded by a corky cambium layer. The course of the leaf-traces through the cortex is peculiar to cycads. The leaf-trace often starts halfway around the stem and is joined at intervals by other traces so that each leaf receives a number of bundles. It is these 'girdling bundles' which give the cycad stem its mechanical strength and rigidity as the amount of secondary wood is very small. Mucilage canals are found in all parts of the plant, in the pith, the cortex, leaves and cone scales.

*Roots*

The taproot of the seedling soon forms several lateral branches which end in smaller fibrous roots. Subterranean species such as *E. ngoyanus, E. caffer* and *E. humilis* have very large tuberous roots. These are probably a climatic adaptation as unlike the columnar species, they do not have stems in which to store water. A feature peculiar to cycads are the apogeotropic roots which grow upwards and form coralloid masses just above the surface of the soil. They are unusual in that they contain a blue-green alga *Anabaena*. These roots appear in the early seedling stage and may develop into a dense mass for a short distance around the base of the old stems. The function of these roots is problematical. It is probably a symbiotic arrangement between the plant and the alga and bacterium which assists the plant in its nitrogen assimilation and fixation. They should not be removed.

*Leaves*

The attractive leaves of the cycad are the feature which gives the plant its popularity as a decorative plant. The leaves have a strong central stalk or rhachis from which numerous leaflets are produced. They are neither strictly opposite nor alternate. When they overlap the direction of the overlap may be either upwards or downwards (see diagram on page 18). The shape, margins (entire or toothed) and colour of the leaflets vary from species to species and serve to distinguish them.

New leaves are very delicate and susceptible to injury, but once they attain their full size, the tissues harden and they become hard and leathery. Both leaves and cones grow with astonishing rapidity and a 1,5-metre-long leaf may take less than a month to grow to its full size. Once the plant is mature, the leaves appear in whorls. Depending on the species the number of leaves in a single whorl may vary from 4 *(E. ngoyanus)* to more than 50 simultaneously *(E. transvenosus)*. The duration of the leafcrown varies with the species and climatic conditions. Leaves may persist for 1, 2 or up to 5 years before a new set emerges. The old leaflets will then yellow and fall off, but the leafstalks may remain for several years (particularly *E. friderici-guilielmi*) before there comes a clean break. It is these persistent leafbases which constitute the outer layer or armor of the stem and which protect the stem from the hazards of fire.

The leaflets of *Encephalartos* have parallel veins unlike the prominent midvein and lateral branching veins of *Stangeria*. The structure of the epidermis of the leaflet is also adapted to the hot, dry climate in which many species grow. The highly cutinized upper surface is almost impervious while the stomata or pores on the under surface of the leaflet are closed except when the air is moist.

*Cones*

Cycads are either male or female and it is not possible to determine the sex in the absence of cones. The female cone is the seedbearing cone while the male cones produce pollen. The female cone is composed of a large number of modified leaves called Sporophylls which are arranged spirally upon an axis. Two ovules (seeds) are attached to each sporophyll (cone scale). The larger cones e.g. *E. natalensis, E. altensteinii, E. transvenosus, E. ferox*, may contain more than 500 seeds in a single cone. The male cones are more slender and also consist of a large number of sporophylls (cone scales) arranged spirally upon an axis. They are very compact at first and elongate with maturity to reveal the microsporangia or pollen sacs on the under surface of the cone scale. When the pollen sacs are mature the pollen is shed. Pollen is produced in large quantities and is comparatively heavy and may be seen laying on the leaves and in the crown of a dehiscing male cone.

*Rates of growth*

Cycads are often referred to as living fossils because they have survived with relatively little modification in their basic character over the past 50 million years. This has led to many misconceptions as to the actual age of individual plants. With the big trees, such as the *Sequoias* of California, the age is determined by counting the annual growth rings. In cycads it is estimated by a study of the persistent leafbases of the stem.

To determine the age it is necessary to count the number of leafbases and to know both the average number of leaves produced in a whorl and the interval that elapsed between successive whorls. This method of estimating age must also take into account the fact that when cones are produced, particularly in female plants, the plant will go into a resting period and may not produce new leaves for 2 or 3 years. In addition seedlings produce only 1 or 2 leaves a year for the first few years and the large whorls of leaves only commence when the plant is 15 to 20 years old.

When counting the leafbases it is necessary to count spirally and not vertically. The interval between new whorls of leaves varies from species to species and also depends on climatic factors. In a high rainfall area such as the Duiwelskloof area, *E. transvenosus* produces new leaves annually. The very tall stems of 10 to 12 m found in this locality may therefore be more or less the same age as the shorter stems of *E. latifrons* where the interval is 4 to 5 years between leaves.

Little scientific research has been done on growth rates and even our botanic gardens where cycads have been grown for 60 years and more, have few records. The stem height of an *E. longifolius* at Kew had reached 3,4 m in 1960. This plant which had been at groundlevel when planted in 1775, had therefore grown at an average annual rate of about 2,5 cm, bearing in mind that the plant was grown entirely under greenhouse conditions throughout this time.

I am indebted to Dr Albert Hertzog for his valuable growth records which show that growth patterns vary not only from species to species but also with individual plants of the same species.

To his regret he only started tagging his plants in 1967 by tying a piece of wire loosely around the stem below each set of new leaves or cones and attaching a metal label with the date and details of leaves or cones. All the plants were in leaf prior to this date and the tags therefore record subsequent new leaves and cones. Although Dr Hertzog's records only cover 7 years, it is clear that no regular pattern exists for a species or for an individual plant despite the fact that the climatic factors and cultural practices were the same for all the plants. Such records by growers in different parts of the country would contribute much needed information to science.

Dr R. A. Dyer of the Botanical Research Institute in Pretoria estimates that individual trunks standing 8 metres tall could be as old as 500 years. He points out that the rootstocks of species which produce suckers from the base in sequence as the stems mature, may attain a far greater age running into thousands of years. At present no satisfactory means of calculating the age of rootstocks in Nature has been devised.

Table showing new leaves (L) and cones (C) as recorded by Dr Albert Hertzog in his garden in Waterkloof, Pretoria.

| | 1967 | 1968 | 1969 | 1970 | 1971 | 1972 |
|---|---|---|---|---|---|---|
| E. altensteinii | L | | L | L | L | LC |
| E. altensteinii | L | | L | LC | L | C |
| E. altensteinii | | | | L | | L |
| E. altensteinii | L | | L | L | | L |
| E. altensteinii | | | L | C | L | C |
| E. altensteinii | | | L | | L | |
| E. ferox | | | C | | L | L |
| E. ferox | L | | | | | L |
| E. ferox | | L | | | | |
| E. eugene-maraisii | C | | | LC | | |
| E. eugene-maraisii | L | | | L | | C |
| E. arenarius | | L | L | | L | |
| E. arenarius | | L | | L | C | L |
| E. longifolius | | L | LC | | | L |
| E. ghellinckii | | L | | | | |
| E. transvenosus | | L | | L | | LC |
| E. laevifolius | | L | | | L | C |
| E. trispinosus | | L | | L | | C |
| E. villosus | L | C | LC | C | C | C |

# Reproduction

*Pollination and fertilization*

Cycads are dioecious which means that the male and female cones occur on separate plants. To produce fertile seed in Nature a male and a female plant must therefore cone at the same time and grow close enough to one another to effect wind pollination. In gardens the very simple technique of handpollination may be practised with the additional advantage that pollen from a male plant growing somewhere else can be used. Experiments are currently being conducted to determine how long deepfrozen pollen remains viable.

Cycad pollen is wind dispersed and because this is a very wasteful method of pollination, immense amounts of pollen are produced. Female cycad cones in nature have a high percentage of fertile seed, so wind pollination is nevertheless highly effective when it does occur. Not only is a copious amount of pollen produced by each male cone but the number of male cones usually outnumber the female cones in those species which produce more than one cone. The male cones seldom all mature at the same time. The 8 male *E. ferox* cones on Colour Plate 26, fig. 1 are in various stages of maturity thereby ensuring that pollen is available over a long period of time.

Insects play a very doubtful role in the pollination of cycads. Bees may be seen collecting pollen from male cones but prolonged observation of a female cone growing only two metres away, produced no evidence of bees visiting the female cone. The female cone does not produce nectar and bees are therefore not attracted to it. The role of the curculionid weevil *Antliarhinus zamiae* in pollination is also doubtful. They certainly parasitize the seeds of cycads but again they are only found on the female cones where they seek out the young immature seeds in which to lay their eggs.

When the male cones are mature they elongate and the cone scales become well spaced so that the pollen may easily be dispersed by the wind. The very woolly male cones of *E. lanatus, E. friderici-guilielmi, E. ghellinckii* bend over to aid dispersal. The pollen is comparatively heavy and may be seen laying in quantity on the adjoining leaves and in the crown. The pollen is then carried by the wind (or human agency) to the female cone, where the cone scales have slightly opened to permit the entry of the pollen. The cone scales and seeds are spirally arranged around the cone stalk, so that once the pollen has entered the cone it is effectively distributed within the cone. The heavy pollen grains gradually sift down between the seeds. The fleshy covering of the seeds is smooth and offers no hindrance to the pollen which must reach the micropyle end of the seed i.e. the end nearest to the cone stalk.

At the time of pollination the ovule secretes a drop of fluid through the micropyle. This fluid traps the pollen grains and as the fluid dries the pollen grains are drawn into the pollen chamber which then closes over. The pollen grain inside the pollen chamber grows and develops and some time later ruptures. A vegetative cell grows out as a pollen tube which penetrates the nucellus. The spermatozoids of cycads are 0,3 mm in size and the largest in either the plant or animal kingdom.

The pollen tube discharges a fluid and the sperms swim through this and enter the egg cell. Some months therefore elapse between pollination and fertilization. This long interval between the initial pollination (the transfer of pollen) and fertilization (the uniting of the male and female elements) is a feature peculiar to Gymnosperms and very different from the relatively rapid process in Angiosperms (flowering plants). In conifers such as the Pine, the seed matures one year after fertilization and two years after pollination.

The fertilized egg cell of the cycad begins to divide and a pro-embryo consisting of a long coiled suspensor develops with the true embryo at the tip. (Diagram p. 24, fig. 2.) It is at this stage, when the embryo consists merely of a bundle of undifferentiated cells at the end of the suspensor, that the seed is shed by the cone. The embryo continues to develop steadily over a period of about six months, filling the entire space previously occupied by the suspensor. At the end of this time the embryo consists of two cotyledons which enclose the plumule (leaf bud) and the radicle (rudimentary root). (Diagram p. 24, fig. 3.)

LONGITUDINAL SECTIONS OF *ENCEPHALARTOS* SEED

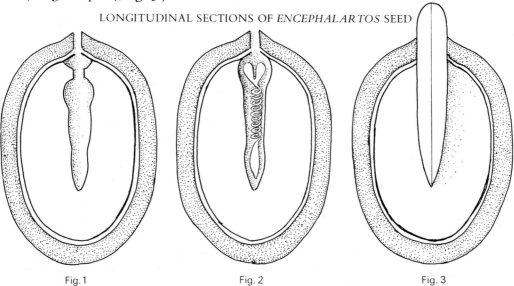

Fig. 1                          Fig. 2                          Fig. 3

*Fig. 1.* A longitudinal section of an infertile seed showing that no embryo has formed. The egg cells in the absence of pollen have withered away and the hollow appears empty.

*Fig. 2.* A longitudinal section of a fertile seed showing the presence of the developing embryo. One of the two egg cells has given rise to a coiled suspensor at the tip of which the pro-embryo has formed. This represents a time lapse of approximately 3 months after pollination and is the stage at which the seed is shed by the cone.

*Fig. 3.* At this stage 6 to 7 months later the radicle emerges from the seed. The two cotyledons are so tightly pressed together that they appear as a single tube. The line shown here is hardly visible to the naked eye.

The cotyledonary tube which consists of the two cotyledons so tightly pressed together that they appear as a solid cylinder now presses against the hard outer covering of the seed. A star shaped crack appears and the radicle emerges from the seed. The seed therefore has no real resting period and develops continuously from fertilization until the root appears.

*Dispersal of the seed*

If all the seed a cycad produces were to remain in close proximity to the mother plant, the seedlings would not only have to grow in the impoverished soil around the mother plant but also compete for space. Nature ensures the dispersal of the seed further afield by providing a brightly coloured fleshy covering which will attract animals. Baboons, vervet monkeys, dassies, birds and fruiteating bats all feed on cycads. In the case of baboons and monkeys, the entire cone is often removed and carried some distance away where the fleshy pulp is consumed and the poisonous kernels are spat out.

Several species of birds feed on cycads particularly the Crowned Hornbill, the Trumpeter Hornbill and the Brown-necked (Cape) Parrot. It is interesting to compare the distribution areas of these three bird species as reported by Roberts with the distribution of the *Encephalartos* species along the eastern side of the country and to realise how closely the one parallels the other. The following firsthand account of the feeding habits of the Crowned Hornbill as reported by Gordon Ranger in The Ostrich, May 1950 is of interest:

'A cycad *Encephalartos* (species probably *E. altensteinii* – author) provides a food item of some importance from late August till late December, the period over which cones of the species (not of the individual) mature. Much hammering with the sharp bill breaks down the large cones and exposes the drupaceous red seeds which are sought principally for the piece of semi-dry flesh detached from one end by pecking and biting; and also for the general covering of the seed which is often partially removed by a shearing action of the edges of the mandibles. The Hornbills carry them off in flight sometimes, often repairing to the ground to deal with them. On the homeward journey from distant excursions, the birds may call at an *Encephalartos* tree and carry seeds away long distances, eating at them during the halts on the way to the roosting site. Rarely, both small and large seeds are found naked below the roosts with insect remains adhering, having been swallowed. Paying constant attention to the ripe cones the family may limit its hunting all day to the near vicinity of an *Encephalartos* tree.'

# Toxicity

The poisonous properties of the South African cycad species may be discussed with separate reference to the stem, leaves and seed.

*Stem*

The stem does not contain any poisonous constituents. The generic name *Encephalartos* is derived from the Greek word *'en'* meaning 'within', *'kephali'* meaning 'head' and *'artos'* meaning 'bread'. Thunberg and other early travellers recorded that the local tribes used these plants as a source of food. Having removed the starchy pith, they tied it in an animal skin, fermented it and then ground it into a meal.

*Leaves*

Although no research studies have been conducted it is doubtful whether the leaves of any *Encephalartos* species are poisonous. The young leaves of all species are freely eaten by sheep, buck, rock rabbits and baboons. The leaves of the Australian genus *Macrozamia* and the American *Zamia* are both extremely poisonous to stock. Observations have shown that cattle eat the young leaves and develop a paralysis of the hind legs. The hind legs drag and when the animal can no longer move about to graze, they die of starvation rather than from the direct effect of the poison. At Government level in Australia, subsidies are provided for the eradication of plants in the grazing areas.

*Seeds*

When discussing the poisonous properties of cycad seeds, a distinction must be made between the fleshy, outer pulp and the actual kernel. Baboons, monkeys, rodents, bats and many fruit eating birds relish them but observations show that once the fleshy red or yellow pulp has been eaten, the hardcoated kernel is discarded or regurgitated, a factor which helps to spread the species locally. The isolated specimen of *Encephalartos ferox* growing in the Makatini Flats in Zululand, 40 km from the nearest *E. ferox* locality, can probably be accounted for in this way. The Trumpeter Hornbill which is common in this area, has been observed to swallow the seeds whole and later regurgitate the kernels. At Modjadji's Kraal the author saw the African children eat the fleshy pulp of *Encephalartos transvenosus*, while in the Eastern Cape the seeds of *E. altensteinii* have been a seasonal addition to the diet of the local tribes for generations.

The kernels of all the species that have been tested, have proved to be extremely toxic. In *The Medicinal and Poisonous Plants of Southern and Eastern Africa* the authors, J. M. Watt and M. G. Breyer-Brandwijk state that the toxic effect appears to be primarily on the liver. Experimental administration of the kernels to rabbits produced listlessness, anorexy and diarrhoea. The post mortem examination showed marked changes in the stomach, liver, lungs and heart tissues. The above researchers tested kernels of *Encephalartos cycadifolius*, *E. friderici-guilielmi*, *E. eugene-maraisii*, *E. ferox*, *E. horridus*, *E. lehmannii*, *E. longifolius* and *E. villosus*.

The common name 'Wildedadel' (Wild Date) which has been used to describe *Encephalartos eugene-maraisii* locally in the Middelburg district, probably refers to the appearance rather than the edibility of cycad seeds.

Children should therefore be warned that the seeds are poisonous and discouraged from eating them.

# Cultivation

*Introduction: Habitat analysis*

To grow cycads successfully in cultivation it is necessary to know the conditions under which they grow in their natural habitats.

*Altitude and frosthardiness*

Cycads grow from sea level in the coastal bush (*E. arenarius, E. altensteinii, E. villosus, E. ferox*) to altitudes in excess of 1 800 m (*E. ghellinckii, E. cycadifolius, E. friderici-guilielmi, E. laevifolius, E. paucidentatus, E. humilis, E. heenanii*).

The latter group all have woolly cones and narrow leaflets (2 to 8 mm) which may be a climatic adaptation to conditions of extreme cold. *E. paucidentatus* and *E. heenenii* which also grow at these altitudes have broader leaflets (2 cm). They grow under forest conditions which affords a measure of protection while the other high altitude species are all found in open grassland in exposed positions.

| Most hardy: | *E. ghellinckii, E. cycadifolius, E. laevifolius, E. friderici-guilielmi, E. lanatus, E. humilis* |
|---|---|
| Reasonably hardy: | *E. inopinus, E. cupidus, E. eugene-maraisii, E. lehmannii, E. princeps, E. horridus, E. trispinosus* |
| Tender: | *E. ngoyanus, E. caffer, E. villosus, E. umbeluziensis, E. longifolius, E. altensteinii, E. lebomboensis, E. woodii, E. natalensis, E. transvenosus, E. paucidentatus, E. heenanii, E. ferox, E. arenarius, E. latifrons.* |

The following rough guide to frosthardiness may be useful:

Most hardy: those species with very narrow leaflets (2 to 8 mm) and a blue-green leafcolour.

Reasonably hardy: those species with medium broad leaflets (1 to 1,5 cm) and a glaucous blue leafcolour.

Tender: those species with medium broad (1 to 1,5 cm) or broader (2 to 4 cm) leaflets and bright green or dark green in colour.

*Rainfall patterns*

Cycads occur only in the summer rainfall areas on the eastern side of South Africa. It is significant that the furthest western species is *E. longifolius* at Humansdorp which is the transitional area between the summer rainfall and winter rainfall patterns. The annual rainfall in the cycad localities varies from 375 mm to 1250 mm and more.

Here too the leafcolour may be used as a rough guide to the amount of rain the species receives in its habitat.

| | |
|---|---|
| 375 to 500 mm | BLUE LEAVES |
| | (Dry inland areas) |
| | *E. cupidus, E. eugene-maraisii, E. lehmannii, E. princeps, E. horridus, E. trispinosus* |
| 500 to 750 mm | BLUE-GREEN LEAVES |
| | (Highveld and inland Cape) |
| | *E. inopinus, E. lanatus, E. friderici-guilielmi* |
| 750 to 1000 mm | BRIGHT GREEN LEAVES |
| | (Coastal and inland areas of Natal) |
| | *E. ngoyanus, E. caffer, E. umbeluziensis, E. altensteinii, E. lebomboensis, E. natalensis, E. heenanii, E. arenarius.* |
| 1000 to 1250 mm+ | DARK GREEN LEAVES |
| | (Coastal and high rainfall mountain forests) |
| | *E. villosus, E. ferox, E. longifolius, E. latifrons, E. woodii, E. humilis, E. laevifolius, E. paucidentatus, E. transvenosus, E. ghellinckii, E. cycadifolius.* |

To sum up by merely looking at the width and the colour of the leaflets, the gardener may form a fairly reliable idea of the cultural requirements of a particular species with regard to frosthardiness and water requirements. It is clear that the above characteristics are a result of the species adaptation to a particular habitat and in some cases to its changing habitat.

Where both blue and green leaved forms of a species occur, e.g. *E. trispinosus, E. longifolius, E. lehmannii, E. princeps* and *E. arenarius.* It will be found that the blue leaved form occurs in the drier inland localities and the green leaved form in the wetter coastal areas.

*E. ghellinckii* and *E. cycadifolius* would seem not to fit the pattern having dark green very narrow leaflets. However both species receive snow in winter in their Drakensberg and Winterberg habitats and this additional moisture results in the dark green leaflets, the very narrow leaflets being an adaptation to the higher altitude and cold.

# Propagation

Cycads may be propagated easily from seed or offsets.

*Growing cycads from seed*

Cycad seeds are fully developed in size before fertilization and the layman therefore finds it difficult to believe that they are not fertile. If he then fails with his first attempt at growing cycad seeds he is often discouraged from trying again. In order to gather fertile seed it is necessary that the male plant coned at the same time as the female plant and that they were growing close enough to effect wind pollination in nature or in the garden.

There are several ways of determining whether the seeds are fertile. If the seeds are fresh i.e. with the red or yellow fleshy covering still adhering, remove the fleshy covering by soaking them in water for two or three days and rubbing it off. Then put them into a deep receptacle filled with water and the heavier fertile seeds will sink to the bottom while the infertile seeds will float on top. The infertile seeds have already started shrinking and the layer of air between the endosperm and the hard shell will cause them to float. With practice and experience the heavier fertile seeds can be judged by hand.

If the seeds are gathered in the veld and the fleshy covering has already decomposed, the water test should not be relied upon. At the stage just before the radicle becomes visible, the outer hard shell has already cracked and air inside the seeds will allow even fertile seed to float.

The only sure (but wasteful) method of determining whether seeds are fertile is to cut them open longitudinally and see whether a fertile embryo is present. The embryo looks like a thin tightly coiled spring (suspensor) and extends to about half the length of the seed. Infertile seeds show only an empty hollow at the micropyle end of the seed. See diagram, p. 24, for fertile and infertile seeds.

Under the discussion on fertilization on page 23 it was pointed out that cycad seeds have no real resting period. Once the ovule is fertilized it develops steadily and continuously. Unlike the seeds of flowering plants where there is a definite resting period and germination has to be initiated by warmth and moisture, cycad seeds start germinating immediately fertilization is complete. By the time the cone breaks open and the seeds are released, the embryo is already at the stage shown in diagram p. 24, fig. 2. The embryo will continue growing steadily whether or not the seeds are planted as in this stage it is nourished wholly by the endosperm within the seed. Several research studies have been done which show the steady development of the embryo from the time the seeds are shed to the stage when the radicle emerges.

## STAGES IN THE DEVELOPMENT OF AN *ENCEPHALARTOS* SEEDLING

*Fig. 1.* A seed showing the emergence of the radicle through the micropyle end of the seed. This represents a time lapse of about 6 to 7 months after the seed was shed by the cone.

*Fig. 2.* As soon as the radicle enters the soil, a tuberous taproot is formed.

*Fig. 3.* Once the taproot is well established in the soil, the hypocotyledonary tube splits open and the first leaf emerges. This is approximately 6 weeks after the emergence of the radicle from the seed. The formation of the coralloid apogeotropic roots is already evident. The seedling is therefore nourished threefold, by the endosperm within the seed, by the coralloid roots on the surface of the soil which assist in nitrogen fixation and by the taproot and the developing lateral roots which absorb nutrients from the soil.

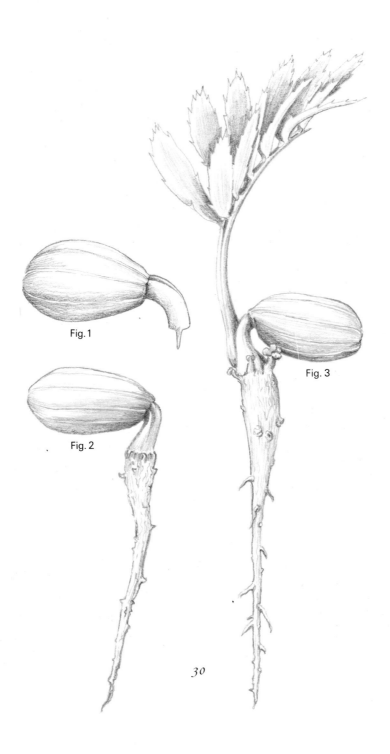

Fig. 1

Fig. 2

Fig. 3

*Fig. 1.* Shows the end which is attached to the cone scale.

*Fig. 2.* Shows the micropyle end of the seed. This opening allows pollen to enter and will later form a star-shaped crack to allow the radicle to emerge. This is typical only of *Encephalartos* species. The outer covering of *Cycas* species cracks longitudinally and the radicle appears to emerge from the side. The star-shaped opening of *Encephalartos* seed is probably an ecological adaptation to prevent the endosperm from drying out, allowing it to nourish the seedling for a long time.

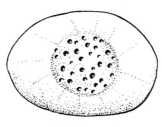

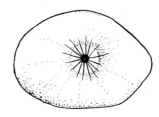

Fig. 1                    Fig. 2

The diagram on page 30 clearly shows in terms of time lapse the rate of development of the seedling.

In practical terms, it is therefore unnecessary and in certain cases inadvisable to plant the seed immediately after the cone breaks up. The hard outer covering is impervious to both moisture and warmth and no real advantage is obtained by planting the seed too early. Among cycad growers there are several firmly established myths on how to hasten germination e.g. soaking the seed in hot water 'to soften the shell' or cracking the seed 'so that water can get in'. Once the physiology and development of the cycad embryo is understood, it is obvious that nature needs no assistance. Cracking the hard outer covering can only lead to dehydration of the endosperm and to the entry of fungal spores which will destroy the endosperm.

Once the cones break open, the seed should not be planted but stored for a period of at least six months. Then carefully inspect the seeds with a good magnifying glass. It will be observed that the star-shaped cracks at the micropyle end of the seed have become more pronounced and raised. (Diagram p. 31.) The seeds can now be planted or one can wait another month until the radicle is actually visible. It is advisable to plant the seeds individually in fairly deep containers so that the seedlings are not disturbed when transplanting them at a later date. The author has found that a series of plastic bags in different sizes is most useful. Cut the bag open carefully and move them annually into the next sized bag. The soil mixture should be a standard potting mixture with adequate sharp sand for drainage and a generous amount of leafmold to ensure that the medium remains friable.

Seeds are pressed lightly into the mixture with two-thirds of the seed above ground. If the radicle is already showing, seeds may be planted at an angle so that the radicle enters the soil and root development can commence.

Note that the radicle is actually the two cotyledons so tightly pressed together that they appear as a solid cylinder. Once the radicle has lengthened outside the seed, it bends towards the soil and the tip of the root emerges from the hypocotyledonary tube. (See diagram p. 30, fig. 1.) At this stage many people assume that the small, brown tip indicates that the 'root' has dried out and is dying.

The root rapidly enlarges once it is in the soil and becomes tuberous with numerous side roots. (Diagram p. 30, fig. 2.) Once the taproot is firmly established the hypocotyledonary tube splits, clearly revealing the two cotyledons and the first leaf emerges. The first leaf may take six weeks or more to appear. It is this hypocotyledonary area, where the leaf joins the root, that is referred to as the rootstock and from whence future suckers will develop.

The larger portion of the two cotyledons remains within the seed absorbing the endosperm and passing it on to the developing seedling. One-year-old seedlings with two or three leaves may still have the seed attached and it should not be removed. Note the seeds present on the seedling plants in fig. 5, Colour Plate B. Leaves continue to appear one at a time for a few months to establish the spiral axis of the trunk. After this they appear in whorls of 3, 5 or 7 until the mature pattern emerges, with 30 to 50 leaves simultaneously in cycles of 2 to 3 years.

Seedling leaves differ markedly from those of the adult plant. Not only are they smaller in size but the shape and the margins of the leaflet are different from that of the adult leaflet. They are usually toothed on both margins and particularly around the apex of the leaflet. The first 3 or 4 seedling leaves are usually small, 15 to 20 cm long including the petiole. The fourth and subsequent leaves are the first true leaves, e.g. in *E. natalensis* and *E. villosus* this leaf may immediately be 50 to 75 cm in length and resemble the adult leaf in characteristics such as prickles on the petiole. All seedling leaves are smooth in texture, the hairy texture of *E. villosus* or *E. caffer* will only manifest itself with the first true leaf. It should be noted that the leaflets of many species that are entire as adults are heavily toothed in the juvenile forms (a period of 10 to 15 years). The leaflets of suckers that arise from the base also differ from those of the mature plant e.g. *E. woodii*, *E. eugene-maraisii* and *E. natalensis*. A chart comparing the first seedling leaves appears on page 47.

The seedlings should be grown in partial shade e.g. a lath roof giving both sun and shade for the first 2 to 3 years. Once they are growing strongly liquid fertilizer will ensure rapid growth. Providing growth is not forced during winter in the colder areas, a sustained rate of growth can be maintained. Cycad seedlings grow much quicker than is generally believed and a plant with a reasonable crown of leaves can be grown in 4 to 5 years from seed.

*Growing cycads from offsets and branches*

Most cycads produce offsets or suckers from the base while others produce branches from higher up the stem. The suckers which arise from the rootstock usually have their own roots. Those that arise out of the stem due to damage, are in fact branches and do not have their own roots as they are connected directly to the vascular system of the main stem. Once they are removed from the stem they have to form their own roots.

*Suckers from the base*

If an established plant produces suckers from the base, open a hole alongside the stem until the whole stem of the sucker and its roots are exposed. Carefully insert a sharp-bladed spade between the sucker and the main stem and slice it off neatly. It should come away intact leaving only a small scar. Dust the cut portion with flowers of sulphur or any other proprietary fungicide and leave the hole open for a few days to allow the damaged portion to dry out and callus before replacing the soil.

Likewise dust fungicide on the wound of the sucker you have removed and leave to dry for a few days. If it is large enough, plant it out in its permanent position in the garden. Smaller suckers or those with insufficient roots should be planted in containers until well established.

In order to induce plants to sucker at the base the following planting method may be adopted. It will be observed in Nature that tall plants that lean usually have numerous offsets at the base. The root system of cycads is not very extensive and the plants are heavy, consequently as soon as they become tall enough to be affected by wind and the weight of the leafcrown, they begin to lean and finally become procumbent. The main root seldom breaks but the tissues at the base of the stem become damaged and it is from these damaged portions that buds arise and develop into new plants complete with their own roots. If a tall stem is therefore planted at a slight angle and supported with a large rock until it has anchored itself, suckering will take place after a few years. On Colour Plate B, fig. 2 numerous offsets from the rootstock can be seen. Note the angle at which the main stem is leaning.

*Removal and re-rooting of branches*

The occurrence of branches higher up on the stem above the ground is less common than below ground suckering. These branches are usually the result of damage to the trunk and when removed have no roots as they are part of the vascular system of the main stem. They should be removed with care, dusted with a fungicide and treated as cuttings i.e. allowed to callus before planting. Plant them by merely resting the cut portion on sharp sand and keep warm and moist until signs of growth are seen. If the leaves are too numerous, reduce the number of leaves but do not remove all the leaves as the plant requires them to manufacture food which in turn will assist in root formation.

Occasionally branches which have aerial roots are seen in nature. The probable explanation for this phenomenon is that at a much earlier stage seeds germinated in the crown of the plant. As the cone decayed the seeds were covered by the decaying vegetable matter and germinated. The roots grew into the soft tissue of the crown and the plant became established. Some of the roots did not penetrate and now appear as aerial roots. When the new whorl of leaves emerged, the young plant was pushed to the side and now appears to be growing out of the side of the stem.

Where the whole crown has broken up into branches the probable explanation is damage to the crown at a stage when it was particularly vulnerable e.g. when new leaves emerge. The damage could have been due to large rocks having been dislodged from a cliff face, large hailstones or the habit of baboons of pulling out the entire crown of new leaves.

*Propagation from leafbases*

Cycads may also be propagated by planting small pieces of the stem attached to the leafbases. This is best illustrated by the experience of one cycad grower who six years previously had removed a cycad of which the crown had rotted and placed it on the compost heap. Further vegetable matter was repeatedly added to the heap which gradually decomposed. Six years later the grower noticed what he took to be seedlings growing on the heap. Carefully removing the humus, he discovered that about twenty 'bulbs' had formed on the portion of stem where the leafbases join the cambium layer. They ranged in size from 4 cm to 8 cm in diameter. One of the smaller ones can be seen on Colour Plate A, fig. 2. One can only assume that the moisture and heat generated by the decomposing compost had provided ideal conditions for this regeneration. This is a field in which further research is necessary.

That the leafbases are capable of other adaptive functions is further borne out by Colour Plate A, fig. 4. The leafbases immediately above the roots show that when the plant has no roots to feed it, the leafbase tissue is capable of compensatory functions, in this case the rudiments of new roots are clearly visible growing from the outer surface of the leafbase.

# Transplanting of mature stems

*Techniques to minimise shock*

Due to the basic xerophytic nature of cycads (hard leathery leaves that do not transpire freely, stored food reserves in the stem and roots and the relatively shallow root system) even mature specimens transplant readily. This should not be interpreted as encouragement to remove mature specimens from their habitat, but on occasion established plants already in cultivation, have of necessity to be transplanted and it would be a pity if such valuable plants died through ignorance of techniques to minimise shock.

The usual procedure is to dig the plant out, cut off all the leaves and the roots and leave it out of ground for a few weeks. The rationale for this severe treatment is obscure. I will probably be disinherited by many collectors if I state that the real reason is that such a plant is then easy to conceal for reasons best known to the collector concerned.

At no stage is a cycad dormant and a plant to be transplanted should be regarded as a live and growing plant to be moved with the least disturbance of its growing functions. Cycads are best moved at the end of summer or early autumn when the annual growth begins to slow down. Water the plant well a week or more in advance so that the roots and stem can take up moisture. If the soil is damp it is easy to expose the roots without damaging them. Species such as *E. villosus, E. caffer, E. ngoyanus* and *E. humilis* have large tuberous roots and special care should be taken when moving them.

Cycad stems are extremely heavy, due not only to the thickened leaf-bases but also to the amount of water stored in the stem. A cycad should be planted no deeper than it had previously been in the soil and it should be well staked to prevent it falling over until the roots have re-established themselves. Even large stems can be adequately supported by tamping the soil well down and placing three or four very large rocks around the stem rather than the usual unsightly anchor ropes. The heavy rocks will also act as a mulch and keep the root area cool and moist and so hasten root development.

Do not cut off all the leaves as plants require leaves to manufacture food which in turn assists root formation. If the leaves are very numerous and the roots have been severely damaged, reduce the number of leaves by a half or a third. The leaves of some cycads will turn yellow and drop off after transplanting e.g. *E. ghellinckii, E. cycadifolius, E. laevifolius*. If the above procedure of watering the plant well prior to lifting is followed and the roots kept damp with wet hessian should there be a delay before replanting, even these difficult species can be safely transplanted.

After transplanting do not overwater the soil at the roots but rather give the damaged roots a chance to heal. Frequent misting of the stem and the leaves is of greater benefit than the time-honoured method of 'puddling' the roots. Many growers wrap the stems in hessian, others have gone further and surrounded the stems with an open cylinder of black plastic filling the space between with damp peatmoss. Both these methods have merit in that the stems have the ability to absorb moisture. The danger however lies in the fact that the dark, damp and warm conditions encourage the development of adventitious roots from between the leafbases and once the cover is removed, these roots die off. It is preferable rather to mist over the stem at intervals and to time the transplanting so that it does not coincide with the hottest part of the year.

The leaves of transplanted cycads are also prone to sunburn particularly if they are moved from a position in semi-shade into the full sun. A light covering of 40% shade cloth will help to harden them off until they are accustomed to the full sun. The same applies to seedling plants that have been bought from a nursery where they have been growing under lath house conditions.

# Pests and diseases

## INSECT PESTS

Insect pests that attack cycads may be classified as follows:

### Those that attack the seeds of cycads

The most common and destructive insect pest is the curculionid weevil *Antliarhinus zamiae*. When the seeds are still completely immature, the female of this species uses her long slender proboscis to drill a hole into the seed. She then turns around and with her ovipositor lays a very large number of eggs inside the seed. They hatch out and completely consume the endosperm of the seed. Seeds from cones of *E. horridus, E. lehmannii* and *E. princeps* which were collected in habitat proved to be almost 100% destroyed on a seed count. When collecting seed from the veld care should be taken not to introduce these weevils into other areas.

### Those that attack the leaves of cycads

The orange and black spotted moth *Zeronopsis leopardina* lays its eggs on the leaves of cycads and the larvae that hatch out in the early spring, feed on the young foliage and reduce the leaves to mere stalks. Museum records indicate that this moth is found only in the Coastal areas from Uitenhage through the Eastern Cape into Natal and inland as far as Eshowe. The injudicious translocating of plants to inland areas will result in this serious pest being introduced into the Transvaal.

In home gardens, mealy bugs, black aphids and brown scale are frequently found on cycad leaves. Any of the proprietary contact insecticides recommended for these pests should be used.

### Those that attack the stems of cycads

Recent importations of cycads from Rhodesia have shown that the stems of such plants frequently have small cylindrical holes. In one plant seen by the author, the infestation was so severe that the plant collapsed and rotted soon afterwards. Plants legally imported under permit are subject to a plant health inspection. Regrettably not all plants are imported legally and one can only stress the total irresponsibility of those involved in introducing foreign insect pests which may become a threat to an already endangered genus.

### Those that attack the roots of cycads

Termites may also attack cycads, but plants that are growing vigorously are less likely to be attacked. Newly planted cycads, that are somewhat shrivelled and particularly if the stems are dried out, should be given protection against termites at the time of planting. All damaged roots should be cut away and the larger cut ends sealed with a paste made of flowers of sulphur and an insecticide.

## DISEASES

Cycads are remarkably free of disease when given the correct cultural treatment required by that species. Those that require full sun and good drainage should not be grown in shade and under the constant drip of trees.

A newly planted cycad will rot if overwatered before the plant has made sufficient roots. All damaged tissue and roots should be cut away and the cut surfaces dusted with flowers of sulphur or a proprietary fungicide and allowed to dry before being planted. 7,5 cm of sharp sand below the stem will assist in root formation and drainage.

Occasionally cycads are seen of which the leaves are striped or discoloured due to a lack of chlorophyll (chlorosis). This is a genetic imbalance and it is not a sign of ill-health or of a soil deficiency.

Cycads are very susceptible to hormone weedkillers particularly those with an oil base. Extreme care should be taken that such weedkillers are not used in the vicinity of cycads.

# Landscaping

Cycads are extremely decorative plants in the garden. Their foliage is both distinctive and evergreen while a female plant in cone will be a feature for several months. They blend in well in an indigenous garden filled with aloes and other succulents, yet are equally at home in a tropical setting with other foliage plants such as palms and tree ferns.

A crowded garden soon loses form and design. Rather than display a collection of cycads (complete with labels!) position each plant so that it adds decorative value to your garden. Shade loving species such as *E. villosus, E. ferox, E. arenarius* and *E. paucidentatus* should be grouped under trees where the shade and moisture will result in more luxuriant foliage than if they are grown in the full sun. Remember that large trees are voracious feeders and the planting holes for the cycads should receive generous amounts of compost. Regular watering and fertilizing is essential if they are to compete successfully with the tree roots.

Blue leaved species such as *E. horridus, E. lehmannii, E. princeps* and *E. eugene-maraisii* should be grown in full sun preferably in rockery conditions as these species require good drainage. The blue colour of the leaves will disappear if they are grown under moist conditions in semi-shade.

Try and group the plants for the best effect e.g. a tall stem with two or three smaller plants at its base will achieve a more harmonious whole than if they were scattered at regular intervals throughout the garden. Very small plants are lost in a general planting and these could be grown in containers until they are larger. By planting them in containers filled with rich compost, they will grow far more quickly than if they are left to grow among other plants.

Frost can be a limiting factor and care should be exercised in choosing species that are at least semi-hardy. Windbreaks on the cold side can be useful as much of the damage is often caused by cold winds particularly to leaves that appeared in late summer and were insufficiently hardened off before the onset of winter. In very cold climates a valuable cycad is perhaps best grown in a container. During summer it can grace the patio and when the cold weather comes it can be moved into a more sheltered position e.g. under the overhang of the roof. Using the traditional Japanese technique of three rollers, large containers can easily be moved across a flat surface such as a slate or brick paving.

One of the most famous potplants in the world is a cycad *E. longifolius* planted at Kew Gardens in 1775 and still flourishing after almost 200 years.

# Varietal forms, hybrids and doubtful species

One is occasionally confronted with a cycad which is difficult to identify positively. Within each species a range of varietal forms occur e.g. *Encephalartos natalensis*, *E. lebomboensis* and *E. villosus* all exhibit several variations, while others are quite distinctly the result of natural hybridization in nature.

The view that these differences within the species merit varietal rank cannot be upheld as they are often merely adaptations to climatic factors e.g. the blue leafcolour of *E. horridus* is less pronounced when these plants are grown in a moist and shady garden, while the blue leafcolour of *E. princeps* is more pronounced at Kirstenbosch where they experience a hot and dry summer. At Kew Gardens, the Jardin des Plantes in Paris, in Bangkok and Singapore the author observed that the length of the leaves, the size of the leaflets and the spacing of the leaflets all changed after the South African *Encephalartos* species had been grown under greenhouse conditions for many years.

The presence or absence of teeth on the margins of the leaflets is one of the most variable factors as the same individual plant will exhibit different patterns during various stages of growth. Plants such as *E. natalensis*, *E. altensteinii*, *E. woodii*, *E. eugene-maraisii* and *E. villosus* will be heavily toothed as juvenile plants and either entire or sparingly toothed when they are mature. When plants are transplanted, particularly when it is a major climatic disturbance as well, the first set of leaves are usually atypical e.g. a plant of *E. villosus* translocated from the forests of Zululand to a dry, inland highveld garden will with the first set of leaves appear to be an *E. villosus* × *E. lebomboensis* hybrid, with darker, shorter and heavily toothed leaflets. Subsequent leaves may be lighter in colour and entire and both sets may then be observed on the plant. Cones may be smaller than average but seldom show any major differences under different climatic conditions.

Where two different species grow together in close proximity, natural hybridization does take place. That it does not take place more often, is difficult to explain as recorded hybrids are very few in number. Regular fieldwork may disclose the fact that only very rarely does the time of coning between the two species coincide. Dare we speculate that nature usually has the 'purity of the species' as a major consideration?

The following hybrids have been recorded. The leaf and cone characters are usually intermediate between the parent species and different forms of the same hybrid also occur. To avoid duplication each hybrid is listed only once in alphabetical order.

*Encephalartos altensteinii* × *E. villosus*
*Encephalartos altensteinii* × *E. trispinosus*
*Encephalartos altensteinii* × *E. arenarius*
*Encephalartos altensteinii* × *E. latifrons*
*Encephalartos horridus* × *E. longifolius*
*Encephalartos lebomboensis* × *E. villosus*

Certain forms which occur in Swaziland which are intermediate between *E. umbeluziensis* × *E. villosus* present a problem. The distribution areas of these two species do not overlap and hybridization therefore seems to be ruled out. Unlike hybrids these intermediate forms are remarkably consistent in leaf and cone detail and it would be reasonable to suggest that they should be regarded as an intermediate species linking *E. umbeluziensis* and *E. villosus*. When one encounters these intermediate forms in gardens, the collectors are usually curiously reticent as to the exact locality of origin and only very extensive fieldwork in this almost inaccessible terrain will solve the problem.

Considerable evidence exists that the concept *E. eugene-maraisii* Verdoorn as presently defined, could well be reviewed. The very scattered distribution areas, separated by several hundred kilometres in some cases and the distinct and constant differences between the Waterberg and Middelburg forms require further investigation. It is possible that the plants from the Wolkberg area may emerge as a distinct new species.

The following differences are constant and constitute a means of identifying the geographical forms of *E. eugene-maraisii*.

*Middelburg form*

1. The rhachis is held upright and erect, the tip does not curl over.
2. The leaflets are set in close V formation.
3. The stems average 2–4 m in height.
4. The leaflets overlap one another downwards.
5. The leafbases of the stem are large and rounded.
6. The lower 20 to 30 cm of the leafstalk is clear of prickles and leaflets.
7. The cones are green in colour with an overlay of fine brown hair.

*Waterberg form*

1. The rhachis is held horizontally and spreading and the tip of the rhachis turns up.
2. The leaflets are set more spreading to the axis.
3. Mature stems seldom exceed 2 metres.
4. The leaflets overlap one another upwards.
5. The leafbases of the stem are smaller and regular.
6. The lower 15 cm of the leafstalk is clear of prickles or leaflets.
7. The cones are almost dark maroon in colour.

Plants superficially resembling *E. laevifolius* have recently been investigated in Swaziland but until sufficient cone material comes to hand no purpose will be served in speculating on the identity of these plants.

The cycads of South Africa have fascinated botanists and gardeners alike for two hundred years and the riddle of *E. woodii* or a lone clump of *E. laevifolius* growing in Northern Natal, will continue to exercise the disciplined mind of the botanist and the free imagination of the collector and unite them in a continued search for further knowledge of these forms of plant life which link the plants of prehistory with those of today.

# Identification by leaf

This key to the *Encephalartos* species uses the median leaflets as the basis for identification of the various species. When one examines a cycad leaf, one notices that the leaflets vary in size and shape along the length of the leafstalk. Those at the top third of the leafstalk are usually smaller and are frequently entire. They are followed by the median leaflets towards the middle of the leafstalk. The lower leaflets are reduced in size and may also have a different shape to the median leaflets. The shape may be so modified that they no longer resemble a leaf and these leaflets are called prickles. One species *E. villosus* has not only a series of prickles but a single 3,5 cm thorn at the base of the leafstalk.

Within a species the median leaflets are usually found to be less variable in size and shape than the top or lower leaflets. The median leaflets therefore form the basis of this key for the identification of the different species.

On the following pages 42–45 full sized leaflets are depicted illustrating the four broad groups in this key. On page 46 a diagram shows the range of leaflets that may occur on a leafstalk. The species shown is *E. woodii* which has the largest range of leaf shapes. The median leaflet in this series would be number 3 or 4 which shows marked lobes on the top margin and smaller lobes on the lower margin. This range of leaflets occurs only on juvenile forms or basal suckers of *E. woodii*, the median leaflets on mature plants are not as broad and are usually entire.

On the same page median leaflets of three ecotypes of *E. villosus* are shown. The short, heavily toothed leaflet is characteristic of plants growing in the drier East London area, the longer but still toothed leaflet, is typical of plants growing in inland Natal, while the long, narrow and almost entire leaflet is characteristic of plants growing under moist forest conditions in Zululand and Swaziland.

*Seedling leaves*

On page 47, 23 seedling leaves of *Encephalartos* and *Stangeria* are depicted. It is regretted that it was not possible to obtain seedling leaves of all the species as a comparison of seedling leaves would throw more light on the relationships between the different species. All adult leaves are in part an adaptation to the ecology of the habitat in terms of rainfall, altitude, climate and whether the plants grow in fertile or infertile soil, in full sun, in semi-shade, etc. These factors do not yet influence and modify the seedling leaf and the seedling leaf may be considered to be the most typical and most constant leaf a cycad produces.

# Median leaflets (Full size)

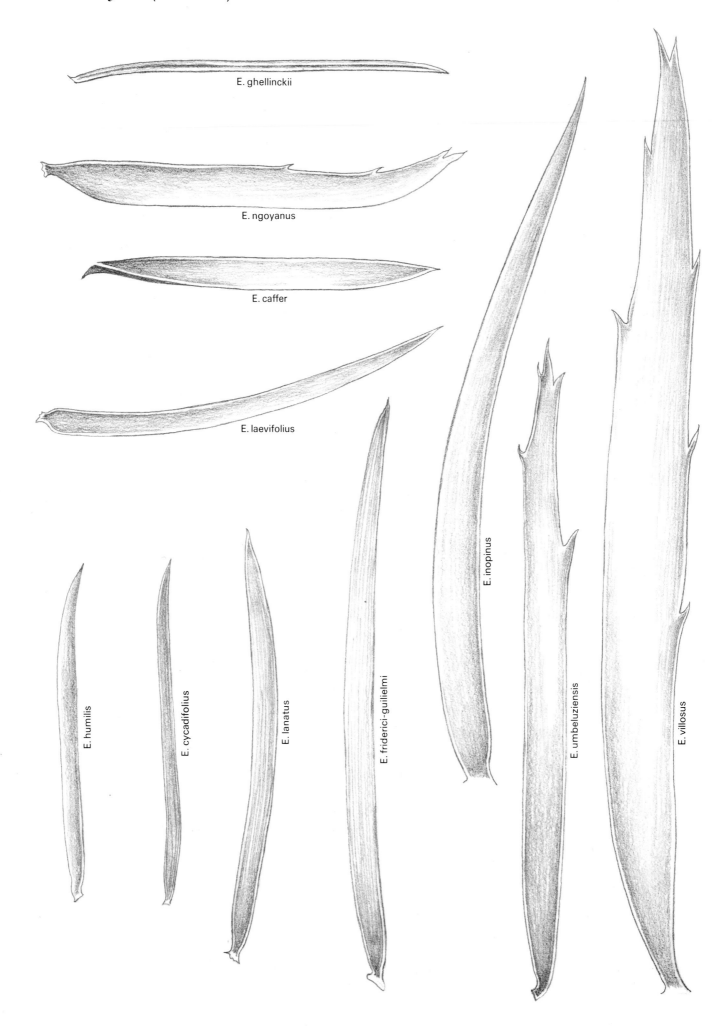

E. ghellinckii

E. ngoyanus

E. caffer

E. laevifolius

E. humilis

E. cycadifolius

E. lanatus

E. friderici-guilielmi

E. inopinus

E. umbeluziensis

E. villosus

*Median leaflets (Full size)*

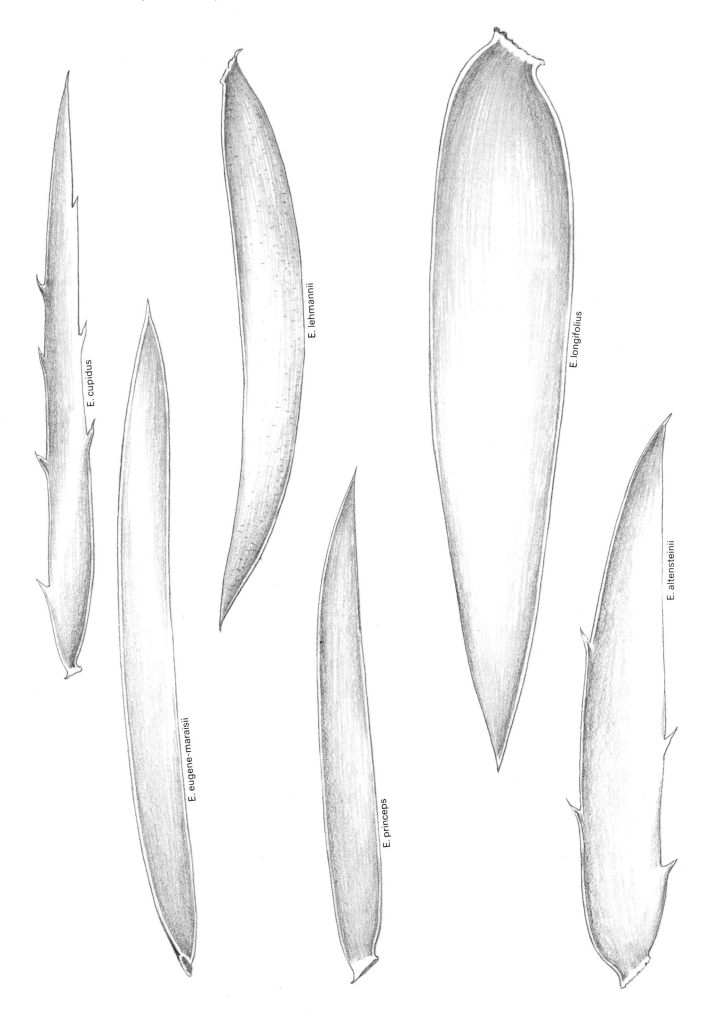

E. cupidus

E. eugene-maraisii

E. lehmannii

E. princeps

E. longifolius

E. altensteinii

# Median leaflets (Full size)

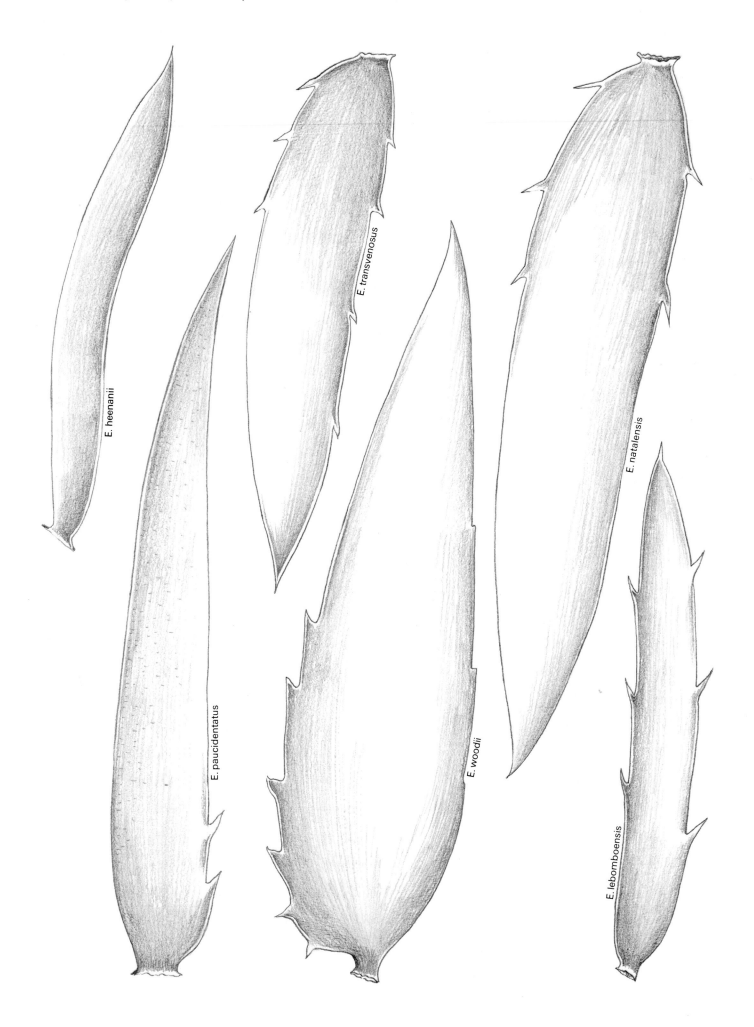

E. heenanii

E. transvenosus

E. natalensis

E. paucidentatus

E. woodii

E. lebomboensis

Median leaflets (Full size)

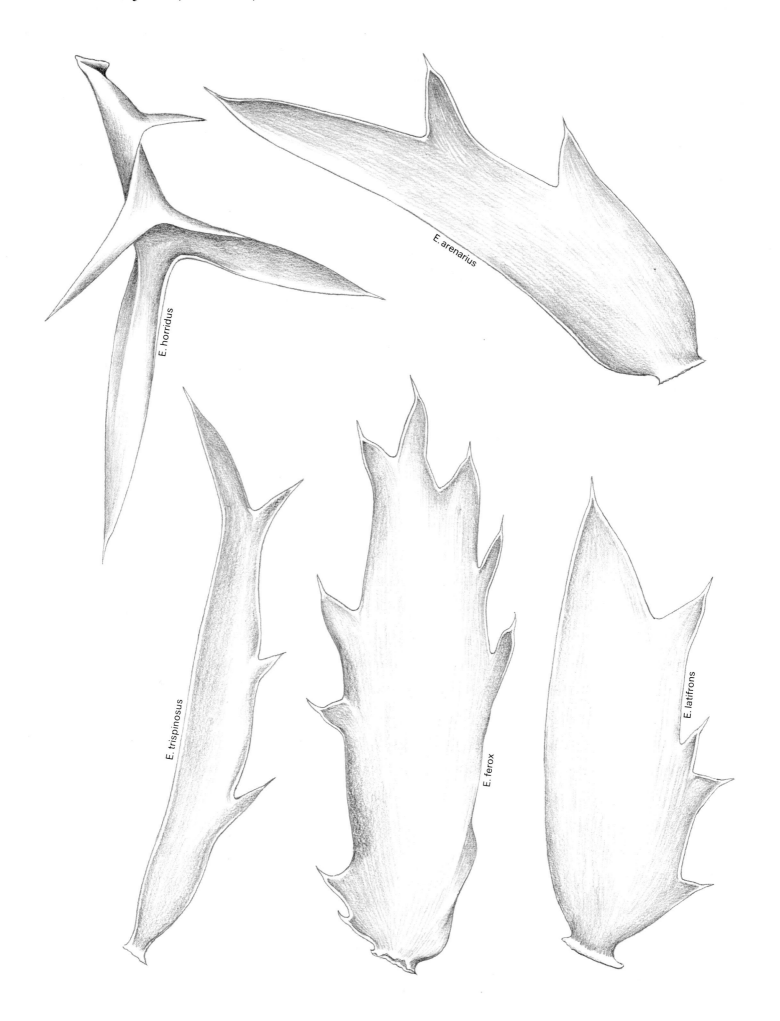

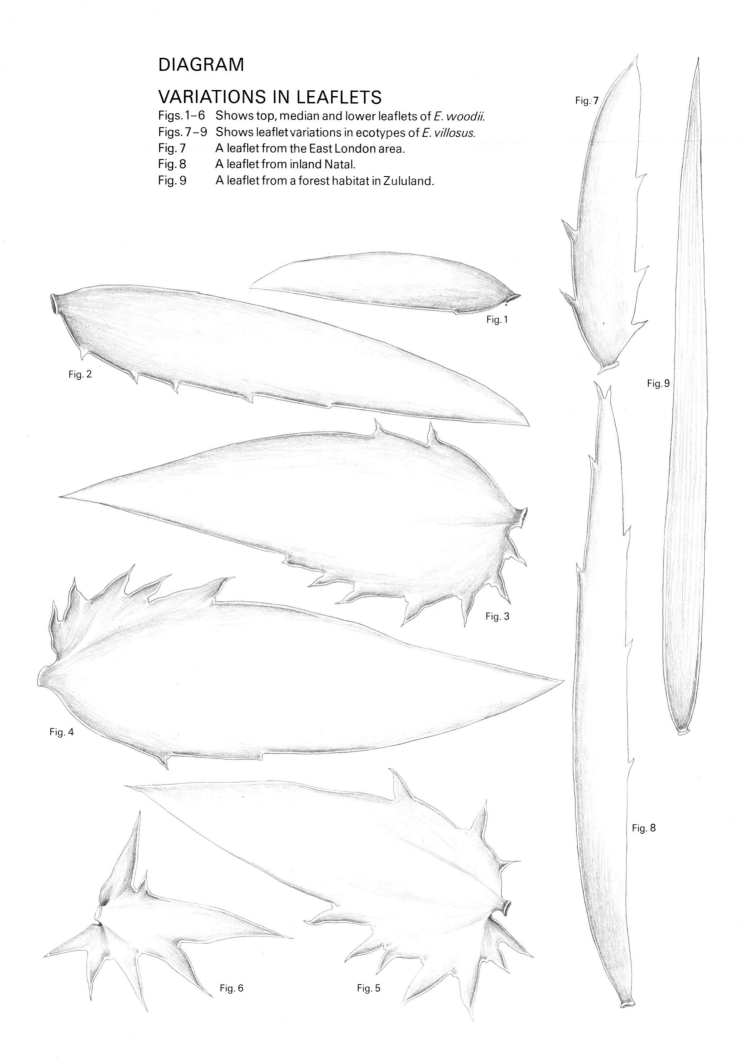

# DIAGRAM

## VARIATIONS IN LEAFLETS

Figs. 1–6   Shows top, median and lower leaflets of *E. woodii.*
Figs. 7–9   Shows leaflet variations in ecotypes of *E. villosus.*
Fig. 7   A leaflet from the East London area.
Fig. 8   A leaflet from inland Natal.
Fig. 9   A leaflet from a forest habitat in Zululand.

Fig. 1

Fig. 2

Fig. 3

Fig. 4

Fig. 5

Fig. 6

Fig. 7

Fig. 8

Fig. 9

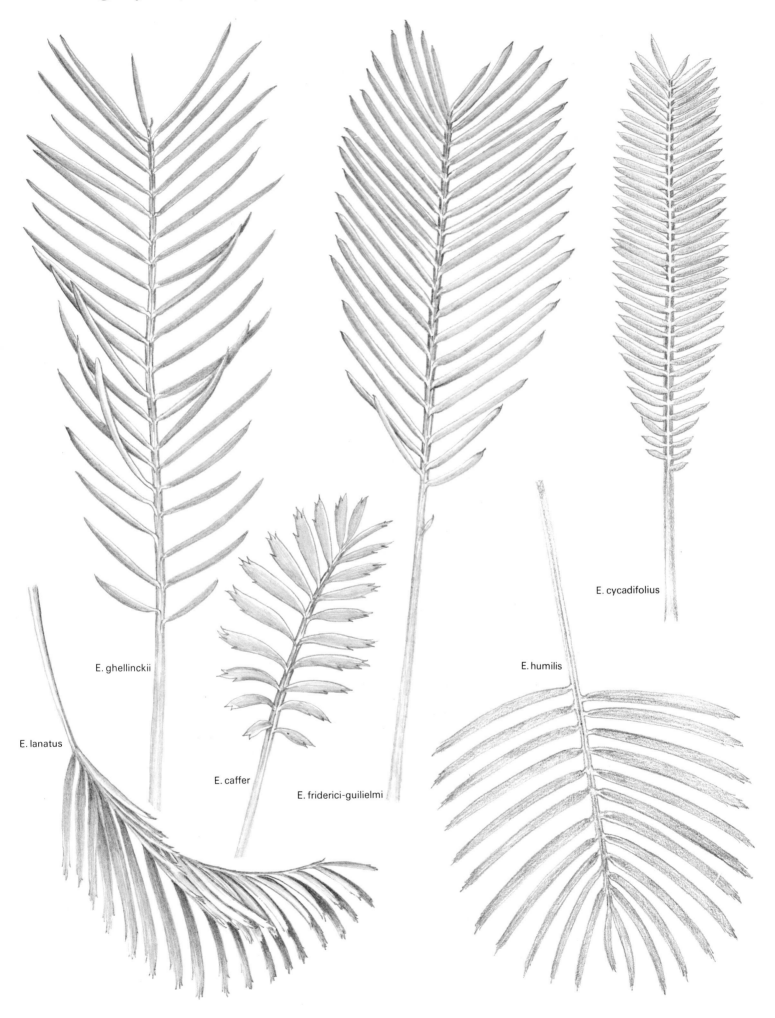

E. ghellinckii

E. lanatus

E. caffer

E. friderici-guilielmi

E. humilis

E. cycadifolius

Seedling leaflets (*Full size*)

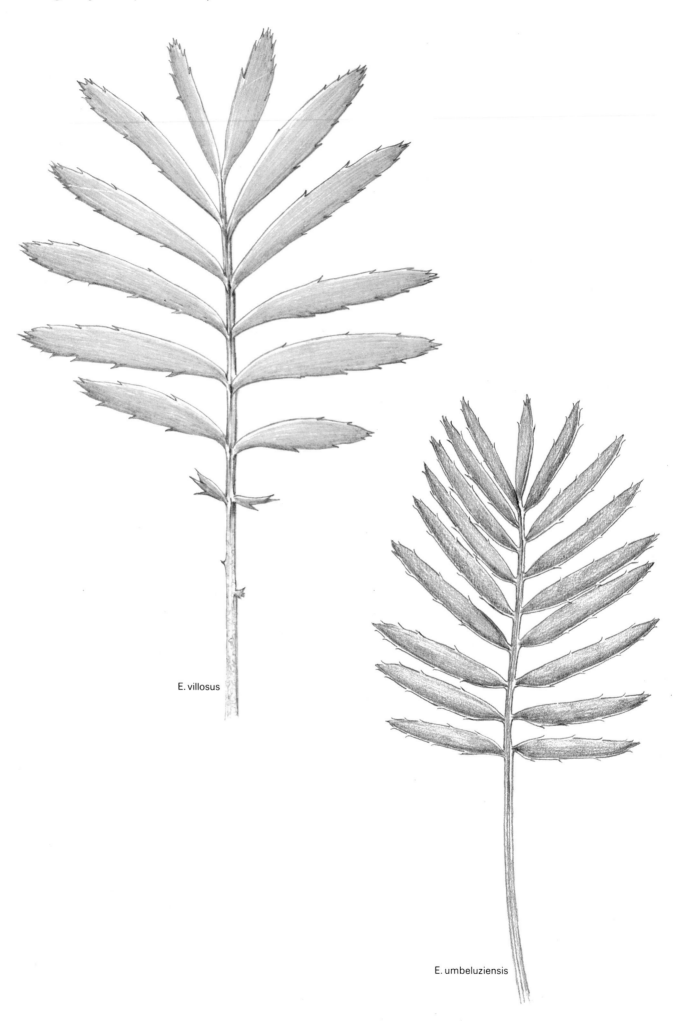

E. villosus

E. umbeluziensis

E. princeps

E. eugene-maraisii

E. cupidus

E. lehmannii

*Seedling leaflets (Full size)*

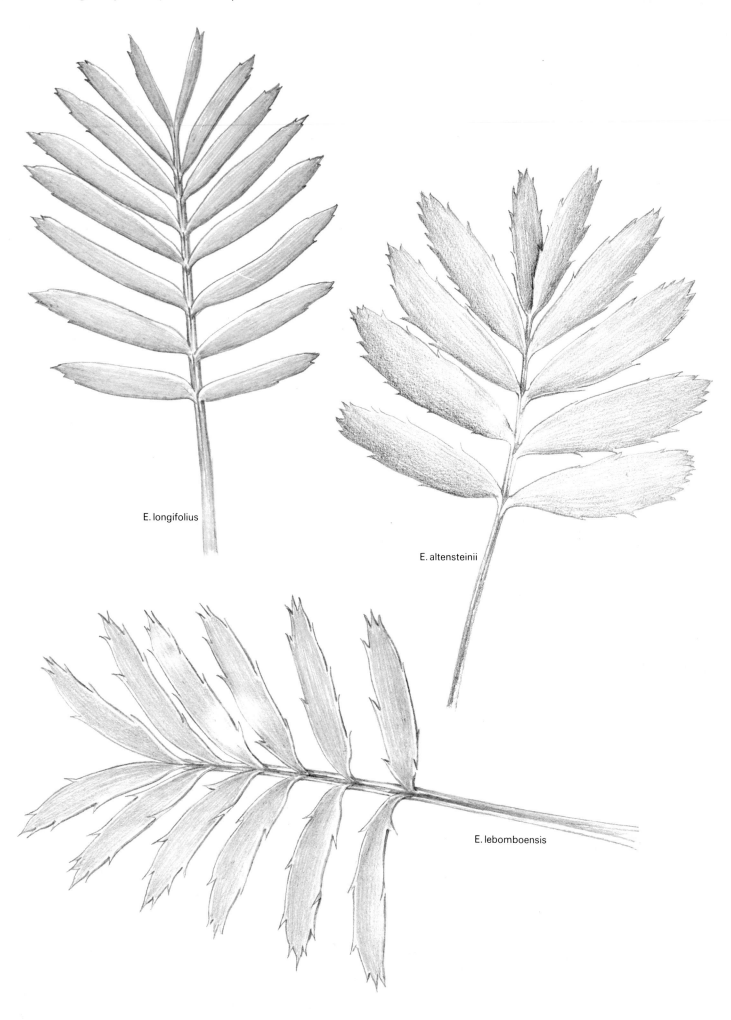

E. longifolius

E. altensteinii

E. lebomboensis

## Seedling leaflets (Full size)

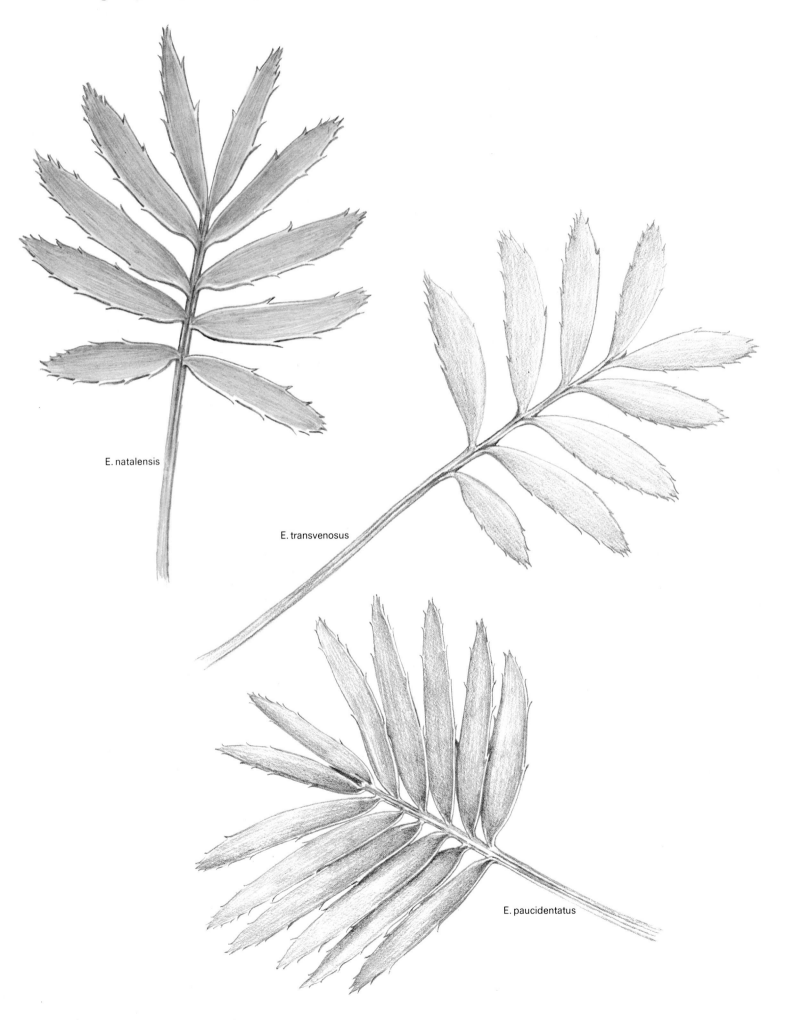

E. natalensis

E. transvenosus

E. paucidentatus

Seedling leaflets (Full size)

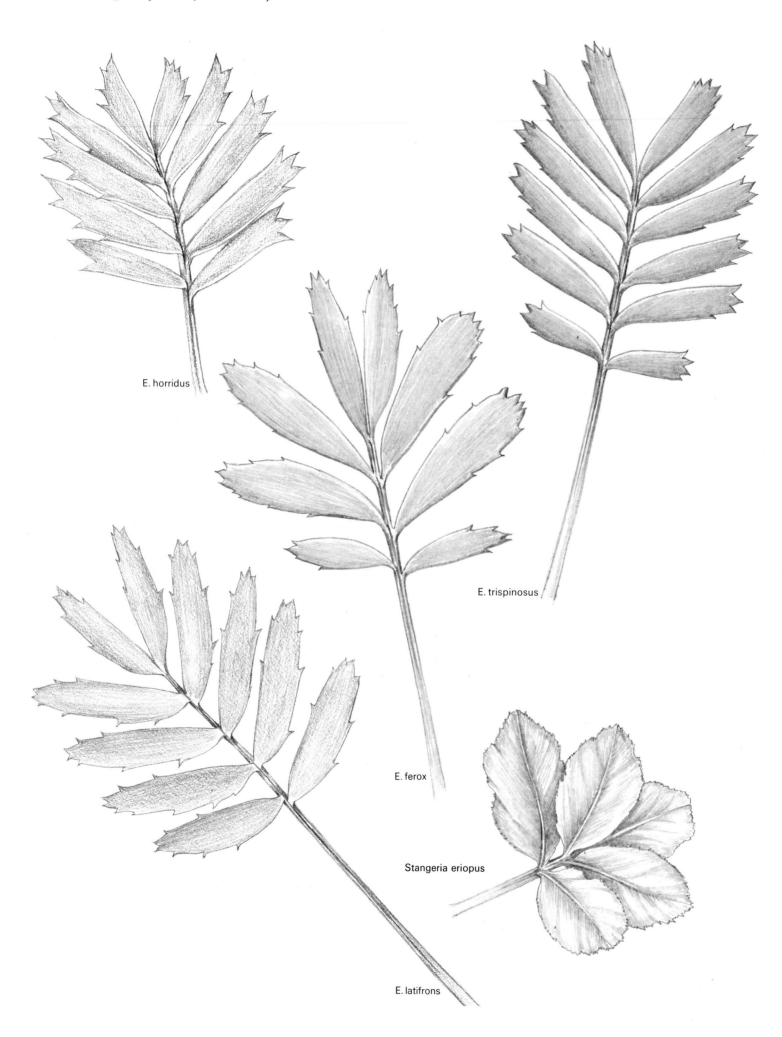

E. horridus

E. trispinosus

E. ferox

Stangeria eriopus

E. latifrons

# Key to the genera of Encephalartos and Stangeria

Two genera belonging to two separate families occur in South Africa.

1. FAMILY: STANGERIACEAE
   Genus: *Stangeria*
   Species: *Stangeria eriopus* (Kunze) Nash
   The stems are subterranean and tuberous; the leaflets are somewhat fernlike. The leaflets have a prominent midvein and branched lateral veins.

2. FAMILY: ZAMIACEAE
   Genus: *Encephalartos*
   Species: 28 species
   The stems are either subterranean (5 species) or up to 10 m and more in height. The stems are characterized by densely packed persistent leafbases. The leaves are pinnate having a central leafstalk with numerous leaflets. The leaflets have parallel veins.

## Key to the species of Encephalartos

This key may be used as an aid to the identification of the species. It attempts to group the plants according to appearance and does not necessarily imply any direct relationships. Any identification made by means of this key should be checked against the full description, illustrations and distribution records. Juvenile forms, atypical plants and hybrids cannot be positively identified using this key.

1. LEAFLETS 2–4 mm BROAD . . . . . . . .    **E. ghellinckii**
   4–10 mm BROAD . . . . . . .    2
   1–1,5 cm BROAD . . . . . . .    9
   2–4,5 cm BROAD . . . . . . .    15

2. LEAFLETS 4–10 mm BROAD, pale green in colour, lower leaflets deflexed . . . . . . . .    **E. inopinus**
   LEAFLETS 4–10 mm BROAD, dark green in colour, lower leaflets ascending or horizontal, not deflexed . . . . . . . . . . . . . .    3

3. Leaflets less than 10 cm in length, stems mainly subterranean . . . . . . . . . . . . .    4
   Leaflets more than 10 cm in length, stems not subterranean . . . . . . . . . . . . . .    5

4. Leaflets well spaced . . . . . . . . . . . .    **E. ngoyanus**
   Leaflets crowded and numerous . . . . . . . .    **E. caffer**

5. Stems well developed above ground, 1–3 m tall 6
Stems not well developed above ground, up to 1 m and suckering freely . . . . . . . . 8
6. Stems and crown markedly woolly . . . . . . 7
Stems and crown not markedly woolly . . . . **E. laevifolius**
7. Leafstalk (rhachis) held straight . . . . . . . **E. friderici-guilielmi**
Leafstalk (rhachis) curls over markedly at the tip **E. lanatus**
8. Leaflet margins thickened, leaflets hard and leathery. . . . . . . . . . . . . . . . **E. cycadifolius**
Leaflet margins not thickened, leaflets soft . . . . **E. humilis**
9. LEAFLETS 1–1,5 cm BROAD
Leaflets 1–1,5 cm broad, without stems aboveground, subterranean, leaves dark glossy green . . . . . . . . . . . . . . 10
Leaflets 1–1,5 cm broad, with well developed stems, leaflets with bluish bloom, which lasts for several months contrasting with older leaves . . . . . . . . . . . . . . . 11
10. Stems subterranean, leaflets toothed and reduced to a series of prickles right to the base of the leafstalk. . . . . . . . . . . . . . . . **E. villosus**
Stems subterranean, leaflets toothed, reduced in size but not to a series of prickles, lower 15 cm of leafstalk bare of prickles or leaflets **E. umbeluziensis**
11. Leaflets blue, markedly toothed on both margins **E. cupidus**
Leaflets blue, may have at most 1 tooth on lower margin only . . . . . . . . . . . . . . 12
12. Leaflets blue, no prominent yellow 'collar' at the base of the leafstalk . . . . . . . . . . 13
Leaflets blue, prominent yellow 'collar' at the base base of the leafstalk . . . . . . . . . 14
13. Rhachis held at 45° angle to the crown, tip of the leaf does not curl over, rhachis straight . . . **E. eugene-maraisii**
Middelburg form

Rhachis held horizontally to the crown, tip of the leaf curls markedly upwards . . . . . . . **E. eugene-maraisii**
Waterberg form

Rhachis twists spirally, tip of the leaf curls over **E. eugene-maraisii**
Wolkberg form

14. Rhachis tip recurves markedly, leaflets in top third of leaf well spaced, large leafbases . . . **E. lehmannii**
Rhachis tip recurves markedly, leaflets in top third of leaf crowded and overlapping, small leafbases . . . . . . . . . . . . . . . **E. princeps**
15. LEAFLETS 2–4,5 cm BROAD
Leaflets 2–4,5 cm broad, may be toothed but not lobed . . . . . . . . . . . . . . . 16
Leaflets 2–4,5 cm broad, with 2 to 5 heavy, triangular lobes . . . . . . . . . . . 23

16. Leaflets held horizontal to the rhachis lower down and in V formation higher up . . . . . . 17

Leaflets held reflexed from the rhachis along the entire length . . . . . . . . . . . . . 21

17. Leaflets reduced in size to base but not to more than one prickle at most . . . . . . . . . . 18

Leaflets reduced in size to a series of prickles . . . 19

18. Leaflets dark green, overlapping in top half, margins entire or sparingly toothed . . . . **E. longifolius**

Leaflets bright green, not overlapping but well spaced in the top half, margins variably toothed . . . . . . . . . . . . . . . **E. altensteinii**

19. Leaflets less than 2,5 cm broad, heavily toothed and overlapping, forming regular pattern of teeth . . . . . . . . . . . . . . . . . **E. lebomboensis**

Leaflets more than 2,5 cm broad, not heavily toothed, may be entire . . . . . . . . 20

20. Leaf crown erect to spreading . . . . . . . **E. natalensis**

Leaf crown with curved rhachis giving umbrella like canopy of leaves . . . . . . . . . **E. woodii**

21. Leaflets reflexed from rhachis, overlapping upwards, markedly toothed, veins not prominent on lower surface of the leaflets . . . **E. transvenosus**

Leaflets reflexed from rhachis, not overlapping, entire or very sparingly toothed, prominent raised veins on under surface of the leaflet 22

22. Leaflets glossy dark green, moderate amount of wool in crown, on stem and leaflets, leaflets usually sparingly toothed . . . . . . . **E. paucidentatus**

Leaflets light green, copious amounts of wool on stem, in crown and on leaflets, leaflets entire **E. heenanii**

23. LEAFLETS 2–4,5 cm BROAD WITH 2 TO 5 HEAVY TRIANGULAR LOBES

Leaflets 2,5 cm broad with 2 to 5 heavy triangular lobes, leaflets glaucous blue . . . . . . 24

Leaflets 2,5–4 cm broad, with 2 to 5 heavy triangular lobes, leaflets green . . . . . . 25

24. Leaflets lobed along the whole length of the rhachis . . . . . . . . . . . . . . . **E. horridus**

Leaflets lobed only in top half of rhachis, leaflets usually entire lower down . . . . . . . **E. trispinosus**

25. Leaflets 2,5–4 cm broad, lobes large but in straight plane with leaflet, leaflet held horizontally to the rhachis, leaflets not overlapping markedly **E. ferox**

Leaflets 2,5–4 cm broad, lobes so large that they twist leaflet out of plane, leaflets overlap markedly and recurve from the rhachis, forming regular pattern . . . . . . . . 26

26. Leaflets dull green with bloom . . . . . . . **E. arenarius**

Leaflets glossy dark green . . . . . . . . . **E. latifrons**

## Identification Table

| Species | Distribution | Maximum stem height | Leaf length | Leaflet width | Leaf colour | Rhachis colour | Leaflets on Petiole | Collar | Cones Number Male | Cones Number Female | Cone colour | Cone texture | Seeds |
|---|---|---|---|---|---|---|---|---|---|---|---|---|---|
| 1. E. ghellinckii | Cape, Natal | 3 m | 1 m | 2–4 mm | dark green | yellow | bare | — | 1–5 | 1–5 | lemon to fawn | woolly | yellow |
| 2. E. inopinus | Transvaal | 3 m (6 m)[1] | 1,5 m | 8 mm | silver-green | yellow | bare | present | 1–3 | 1–2 | silver-green | smooth | apricot |
| 3. E. ngoyanus | Natal | subterranean | 0,5–1,25 m | 8 mm | dark green | green | reduced | — | solitary | solitary | yellow | smooth | red |
| 4. E. caffer | Eastern Cape | subterranean | 0,5–1 m | 7 mm | fresh green | green | prickles | — | solitary | solitary | yellow | smooth | red |
| 5. E. laevifolius | Transvaal, Swaziland | 3 m | 1,5 m | 7 mm | dark green[2] | yellow | bare | — | 1–6 | 1–5 | yellow | smooth[6] | yellow |
| 6. E. friderici-guilielmi | Easter Cape | 4 m | 1–1,5 m | 7–8 mm | dark green | green | reduced | — | 1–12 | 5 | yellow | woolly | yellow |
| 7. E. lanatus | Transvaal | 1,5 m | 1 m | 6–8 mm | soft green | green | reduced | — | 1–4 | 1–4 | yellow | woolly | yellow |
| 8. E. cycadifolius | Eastern Cape | – 1 m | – 1 m | 4–6 mm | dark green | yellow | bare | — | 1–2 | 1–2 | yellow | woolly | yellow |
| 9. E. humilis | Transvaal | subterranean | 30–50 cm | 4–6 mm | dark green | yellow | bare | — | solitary | solitary | fawn to brown | woolly | yellow |
| 10. E. villosus | Cape, Natal, Transvaal, Swaziland | subterranean | 1,5–3 m | 1,5–2 cm | dark green | green | prickles | — | 1–8 | 1–4 | dark yellow | smooth | red |
| 11. E. umbeluziensis | Swaziland | subterranean | 1–2 m | 1,0–1,5 cm | bright green | green | bare | — | 1–4 | 1–4 | green | smooth | apricot |
| 12. E. cupidus | Transvaal | 25 cm | 1 m | 1,5 cm | blue | blue | reduced | — | 1–3 | 1–2 | green | smooth | apricot |
| 13. E. eugene-maraisii | Transvaal | 4 m (6 m)[1] | 1–1,5 m | 1,5 cm | blue | blue | bare | — | 1–8 | 1–5 | brown to maroon[5] | smooth | amber brown |
| 14. E. lehmannii | Eastern Cape | 1,5 m | 1–1,5 m | 1,5–2 cm | blue[3] | blue | bare | present | solitary | solitary | green over black | smooth | red |
| 15. E. princeps | Eastern Cape | 4 m | 1–1,3 m | 1,5 cm | blue[3] | blue | bare | present | 1–3 | 1–3 | dark olive-green | smooth | red |
| 16. E. longifolius | Eastern Cape | 4 m | 1–2 m | 2–3 cm | dark green[2] | yellow | bare | present | 1–3 | 1–3 | dark olive-green | smooth | red |
| 17. E. altensteinii | Eastern Cape | 5 m (7 m)[1] | 1–2 m | 2,5 cm | bright green | green | bare | present | 1–5 | 1–5 | dark yellow | smooth[6] | red |
| 18. E. lebomboensis | Natal, Transvaal, Swaziland | 4 m | 1–2 m | 1,5 cm | bright green | green | prickles | — | 1–3 | 1–3 | yellow-orange | smooth | red |
| 19. E. natalensis | Natal | 4 m (6 m)[1] | 1,5–3 m | 2,5–4 cm | dark green | green | prickles | — | 1–5 | 1–5 | dark yellow | smooth[6] | red |
| 20. E. woodii | Natal | 6 m | 2–2,5 m | 4–6 cm | dark green | green | prickles | — | 1–6 | — | yellow-orange | smooth[6] | — |
| 21. E. transvenosus | Transvaal | 8 m (13 m)[1] | 1,5–2,5 m | 2,5–4 cm | dark green | yellow | prickles | — | 1–4 | 1–4 | yellow-orange | slightly woolly | red |
| 22. E. paucidentatus | Transvaal, Swaziland | 6 m | 1,5–2,5 m | 2,5–3 cm | dark green | yellow | bare | — | 1–5 | 1–5 | yellow-orange | slightly woolly | red |
| 23. E. heenanii | Transvaal, Swaziland | 3 m | 1–1,3 m | 1,5–2 cm | pale green | green | reduced | — | 1–3 | 1–3 | dark yellow | woolly | red |
| 24. E. horridus | Eastern Cape | – 0,5 m | – 1 m | 2,5–4 cm | blue | blue | bare | present | solitary | solitary | maroon | smooth | red |
| 25. E. trispinosus | Eastern Cape | – 1 m | 1–1,25 m | 1,5–2,5 cm | blue[3] | blue | bare | present | solitary | solitary | bright yellow | smooth | red |
| 26. E. ferox | Natal, Mozambique | – 1 m (2 m)[1] | 1–2 m | 3–5 cm | dark green | green | prickles | — | 1–10 | 1–5 | red | smooth | red |
| 27. E. arenarius | Eastern Cape | – 1 m | 1–1,5 m | 3–4 cm | mid-green[2] | green | bare | — | solitary | solitary | green | smooth | red |
| 28. E. latifrons | Eastern Cape | 3 m | 1–1,5 m | 4–6 cm | dark green | yellow | bare | — | 1–3 | 1–3 | dark olive-green | smooth | red |

1. The figure in brackets denotes exceptionally tall stems.
2. In certain localities the leaf colour may be blue.
3. In certain localities the leaf colour may be green.
4. Certain species have a yellow band or "collar" at the base.
5. Cone colour varies according to geographical forms. Waterberg form is maroon, Middelburg form greeny-grey, Wolkberg form yellow.
6. Although the texture is smooth at maturity, cones are slightly velvety at first.

# Morphology of Cycads

## (See Plate A)

**Fig. 1.**
*Male cone of E. ferox.* Note the pollen sacs on the lower surface of the cone scales. The scales are well spaced to allow wind dispersal of pollen.

**Fig. 2.**
This shows a young plant which developed from the inner wall of the stem between the leafbases and the cambium layer.

**Fig. 3.**
*Male cone of E. friderici-guilielmi.* The pollen sacs on the lower surface of the cone scales are just visible through the dense wool covering the cone.

**Fig. 4.**
Once the taproots of a cycad are damaged when transplanting, numerous smaller roots develop. Note also the adventitious rootlets developing on the outer surface of the leafscales.

**Fig. 5.**
*Female cone of E. cycadifolius.* The thick wool on the female cones parts slightly at maturity to allow the entry of pollen. The wooly cones are an adaptation to extreme cold.

**Fig. 6.**
A transverse section of a cycad stem showing the spirally arranged leafbases, the corky cambium layer, the very thin layer of secondary wood and the large pith. The shiny dots in the pith and cambium are drops of mucilage exuded by the mucilage canals.

# Damage and Regrowth

## (See Plate B)

**Fig. 1.**
This plant of *E. eugene-maraisii* was severely burnt by fire and then mutilated in an attempt to remove it. It has since grown several suckers from the base and a growth bud can be seen growing from the cut in the stem. Note that the leaflets of the suckers are heavily toothed.

**Fig. 2.**
Eight suckers of varying sizes have grown from the base of this plant of *E. inopinus.* Note the damaged and leaning stem.

**Fig. 3.**
The damage to the stem of this *E. cycadifolius* was caused by porcupines.

**Fig. 4.**
The crown of this *E. humilis* had completely rotted away. Regeneration in the form of three new crowns and several suckers from the base has taken place.

**Fig. 6.**
Baboons have damaged the immature female cone of this *E. longifolius.* The leaves in the foreground have turned brown due to the damage caused by the baboons who use the leaves to climb up into the centre of the plant.

**Fig. 5.**
Young seedlings in a commercial nursery illustrating practical conservation through cultivation. Note that the seeds still adhere to the seedlings 18 months after planting.

# Plate 1. *Encephalartos ghellinckii* Lem.

*Distribution:* CAPE and NATAL

*Encephalartos ghellinckii* occurs in the Transkei in the districts of Tabankulu and Flagstaff and along the southern foothills of the Drakensberg northwards to Mont-aux-Sources in the Natal Drakensberg. Plants are usually found growing in open grassland on a southern or eastern slope. Rainfall varies from 1000 – 1250 mm per annum. Winters are very cold with frost and snow.

*Stem:* Stems may be up to 3 m in height with a diameter of 30 to 40 cm. Older plants with tall stems often lean and become procumbent. It has an open woolly crown with the wool persisting at all times.

*Leaves:* The leaves are 1 m long and the bright yellow rhachis is spirally twisted. The median leaflets are 8 to 14 mm long and 2 to 4 mm broad. The margins of the leaflets are entire and revolute. This rolling back of the margin is found in no other species. New leaves are densely covered with grey wool, but this disappears with age and the mature leaves are bright green.

*Cones:* Up to five cones have been recorded. They are densely woolly, pale lemon at first and turning a tawny-beige with age. The male cones are 20 to 25 cm long and 6 to 8 cm in diameter. The female cones are 20 to 25 cm long and 12 to 15 cm in diameter.

*Seeds:* Golden-yellow.

*Affinities:* The two nearest related South African species are *Encephalartos cycadifolius* and *E. friderici-guilielmi*. They also have densely woolly cones but the median leaflets are much broader and not revolute like those of *Encephalartos ghellinckii*.

The cultivated Japanese species *Cycas revoluta* may also cause confusion.

1. The dark green glossy leaflets of *Cycas revoluta* have a prominent midvein, all the *Encephalartos species* lack this midvein.

2. The seeds of *Cycas revoluta* are held in a loose stalked cluster and are not enclosed in a compact cone.

*Cultivation:* This is a difficult species to re-establish or maintain in cultivation due to its very specific habitat conditions. If mature plants are transplanted the leaves turn yellow and new leaves may take as long as four to five years to appear. Coning is rare in cultivation. *Encephalartos ghellinckii* should be grown in a shady position with a cool, moist root run. The soil mixture should be slightly acid. A thick mulch of old grass will keep the soil cool and moist. This species is completely hardy.

The specific name honours M. Ed. de Ghellinck de Wolle, a noted amateur horticulturalist at the time in Ghent.

# Plate 1. E. ghellinckii. Lem.

1. Plant in habitat.
2. Male cones.
3. Leaf detail. Note the wool in the crown.
4. Female cone.

*Plate 2. E. inopinus.* R. A. Dyer

1. Female cone.
2. Leaf detail. Note that the leaflets are deflexed.
3. Male cones.
4. Plant in habitat.
5. Stem detail. Mixed large and small leafbases indicate lean years in nature.

# Plate 2. *Encephalartos inopinus* R. A. Dyer

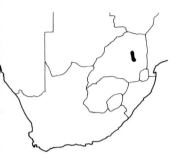

*Distribution:* TRANSVAAL
Field records to date point to an extremely restricted distribution area in the Lydenburg district of the Eastern Transvaal. It grows in hot, dry valleys where the annual rainfall seldom exceeds 375 mm.

*Stem:* Stems are usually up to 3 m in height. Several stems up to 6 m in length have been recorded but these are procumbent. Plants sucker freely from the base. The stem is very characteristic, a tawny-beige colour with mixed large and small leafscales which give a 'patchwork' effect. The stems are slender with a diameter of 15 to 25 cm and they lean from an early age.

*Leaves:* The leaves are 1 to 1,5 m long with a straight yellow rhachis. The rhachis has a spiral twist along its length and this gives a graceful feathery effect to the leafcrown. The median leaflets are entire, 14 to 20 cm long and 8 to 10 mm broad. The angle of the lower leaflets is deflexed from the rhachis, a characteristic not seen in any other South African cycad. The leaf colour is a fresh silvery-green.

*Cones:* Up to three cones have been recorded. The cones are the same silvery-green colour as the leaves even at maturity. Male cones are 18 to 25 cm long and 6 to 8 cm in diameter. The female cones are 30 to 35 cm long and 15 to 20 cm in diameter. The terminal facets of the cone scales are thickly covered with small white, raised papillae giving a silvery matt appearance to the terminal facet. The surrounding upper and lower facets are a shiny green colour.

*Seeds:* Apricot coloured.

*Affinities: Encephalartos inopinus* differs in many respects from all other South African species and bears a marked resemblance to the Mexican genus *Dioon*. The graceful downward curve of the lower leaflets and the upward spread of the top leaflets, is quite distinctive as is the matt surface of the cone scales.

*Cultivation:* Due to extreme climatic conditions, coning has not taken place for several years in its habitat and disturbed plants in cultivation coned for the first time eight years after planting. Active regeneration is not taking place in the veld and this species must therefore be considered in need of stringent protection. As plants already in cultivation settle down and coning cycles become established, a source of fertile seed through hard pollination will emerge to re-establish the species in numbers and ensure its survival.

The specific name '*inopinus*' means '*unexpected*' a reference to its type locality, the farm '*Onverwacht*' and a comment on the unexpectedness of discovering a new cycad species at this late stage of botanical discovery in South Africa.

# Plate 3. *Encephalartos ngoyanus* Verdoorn

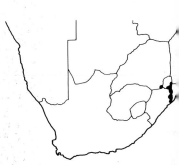

*Distribution:* NATAL, TRANSVAAL and SWAZILAND

*Encephalartos ngoyanus* grows in open grassveld and forest margins in Zululand in the districts of Ngoye, Mtunzini and northwards through Mkuzi into the south eastern Transvaal and Swaziland. It is frequently found growing between boulders but these plants might just be the survivors of grass fires.

*Stem:* *Encephalartos ngoyanus* is usually subterranean with a markedly tuberous root system. The crowns are occasionally exposed and may reach 30 cm in height with a diameter of 15 to 20 cm.

*Leaves:* Leaves are dark green 0,5 to 1,25 m in length. The rhachis is straight and the leaflets are well spaced. The median leaflets are 7 to 10 cm long and 8 mm broad, usually with one or more teeth on the lower margin and rarely entire. They are reduced in size but not to a series of prickles.

*Cones:* The cones are solitary and dark yellow. The male cones are 20 to 25 cm long and 5 to 7 cm in diameter. Female cones are 25 cm long and 12 to 15 cm in diameter. The cone scales are flattened and slightly overlap the lower ones. The lower margin of the scale is smooth and not fringed.

*Seeds:* Shiny red.

*Affinities:* *Encephalartos ngoyanus* nearest relative is *E. caffer* from the Eastern Cape though their localities are almost 1 000 kilometres apart. *Encephalartos ngoyanus* may be distinguished as follows:

1. The leaflets of *Encephalartos ngoyanus* are usually toothed and seldom entire, while those of *E. caffer* are usually entire and only toothed in seedlings.

2. The leaflets of *Encephalartos ngoyanus* are a dark glossy green and the leaflets are well spaced on the rhachis. The leaflets of *Encephalartos caffer* are a soft, fresh green, slightly hairy and so numerous that they give a ruffled effect.

3. The female cone scales of *Encephalartos ngoyanus* overlap the lower ones, while those of *E. caffer* have a terminal facet. The cones of both species are green and turn yellow at maturity.

*Cultivation:* *Encephalartos ngoyanus* grows well in cultivation but is not a vigorous grower and seldom has more than 8 to 10 leaves to a crown. It is often deciduous before new leaves or cones emerge. It prefers slightly dry conditions and should be grown in full sun and may be classed as semi-hardy.

The specific name 'ngoyanus' refers to the type locality Ngoye in Zululand.

*Plate 3. E. ngoyanus.* Verdoorn

1

2

1. Plant in habitat.
2. Leaf detail.
3. Male cone.
4. Female cone.

3

4

## Plate 4. *E. caffer*. (Thunb.) Lehm.

1. Plant in habitat.
2. Leaf detail.
3. Male cone.
4. Female cone.
5. New leaves.

# Plate 4. *Encephalartos caffer* (Thunb.) Lehm.

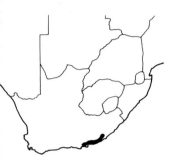

*Distribution:* EASTERN CAPE

*E. caffer* occurs in sour grassveld in the districts of Humansdorp, Alexandria, Bathurst, East London and Kentani. Summer rainfall varies from 1 000 mm at the coast to considerably less inland. Summer temperatures are high and no frost occurs.

*Stem:* Encephalartos caffer is a subterranean species with a heavy tuberous root system. The portion of the stem below ground may be quite considerable, 30 to 40 cm in length and 20 to 25 cm in diameter. The crown is woolly at all times.

*Leaves:* Leaves of *E. caffer* are 50 cm to 1 m in length and a fresh light green. The leaves are very woolly at first and are never entirely smooth or glossy. The rhachis is straight but the leaves are so numerous that the lower leaves are held almost horizontally. Median leaflets are 8 to 10 cm long and 10 mm broad. They are usually entire except in the juvenile form when one or two teeth occur on both margins. The leaflets are so numerous and crowded on the rhachis that they give a ruffled effect to the leaf.

*Cones:* Both male and female cones are solitary and greeny-yellow at maturity. Male cones are 20 to 30 cm long and 7 to 12 cm in diameter. Female cones are 30 cm long and 15 cm in diameter. The female cone scales have a flat terminal facet with a slight raised and toothed margin.

*Seeds:* Bright red and glossy.

*Affinities: Encephalartos caffer* is closely related to *E. ngoyanus,* but is readily distinguished as follows:

1. The leaves and crown of *E. caffer* are woolly and hairy at all stages. *E. ngoyanus* has smooth, glossy dark green leaves.

2. The leaflets of *Encephalartos caffer* are usually entire and thickly crowded to give a ruffled effect, those of *E. ngoyanus* are toothed and well spaced on the rhachis.

3. Both the male and female cones of *Encephalartos caffer* have a well defined flat terminal facet, while those of *E. ngoyanus* are flattened and overlap the lower scales.

*Cultivation: Encephalartos caffer* grows well in cultivation but may be slow to re-establish. It requires a slightly acid soil mixture, rich in organic matter and ample moisture should be given. It may be grown in full sun and is semi-hardy to frost.

# Plate 5. *Encephalartos laevifolius* Stapf and Burtt Davy

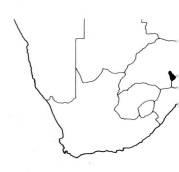

*Distribution:* EASTERN TRANSVAAL and SWAZILAND

*Encephalartos laevifolius* is restricted to the Kaapsche Hoop Mountains in the Nelspruit district and the Piggs Peak area of Swaziland. This is a high rainfall area with an annual rainfall of more than 1250 mm. *Encephalartos laevifolius* grows on exposed rocky outcrops at an altitude of 1800 m. Frost occurs in winter.

*Stem:* *Encephalartos laevifolius* has a tall stem up to 3 m and occasionally up to 4 m. The stem is characterized by the even, regularly patterned leafbases and the stems are slender in comparison to other columnar species. The stem and crown show very little wool. Plants sucker freely from the base.

*Leaves:* The dark green leaves are up to 1,5 m long with a straight markedly yellow rhachis, which may twist in the upper third. Leaflets are 12 to 15 cm long and 5 to 7 mm broad. Near the base of the rhachis they lie horizontally to the rhachis and only assume a V disposition in the top half of the leaf. Leaflets are entire and blue-green with a slight bloom on the top surface only, this soon disappears and they become dark green.

*Cones:* One to five cones have been recorded which are only slightly woolly at first and soon become smooth. Male cones are 30 to 40 cm long and 10 cm in diameter. At maturity the male cones are curved. The female cones are 20 to 30 cm long and 12 to 15 cm in diameter. Short white hairs densely cover the terminal facet making it appear lighter in colour

*Seeds:* Orange-yellow.

*Affinities:* *Encephalartos laevifolius* may be confused with *E. lanatus* in cultivation but not in the field as the former grows in the Eastern Transvaal in the catchment of the Crocodile River while the latter is restricted to the catchment of the Olifants River in the Central Transvaal. It differs from *Encephalartos lanatus* in the following respects:

1. *Encephalartos laevifolius* has tall, slender stems with regular, smooth leafbases, while *E. lanatus* is a medium tall plant seldom exceeding 1,5 m and the stems are consistently woolly at all times.

2. The leafcrown of *Encephalartos laevifolius* is erect at first but soon drops to a horizontal position while the leaves of *E. lanatus* are sharply recurred at the tips.

3. The leaflets of *Encephalartos laevifolius* are held horizontally to the markedly yellow rhachis and only assume a V disposition in the top third, those of *E. lanatus* are held in a tight V formation along the entire length of the rhachis.

4. The cones of *Encephalartos laevifolius* are smooth compared to those of *E. lanatus* which are markedly woolly even at maturity.

*Cultivation:* Plants in cultivation grow well and are easy to re-establish after transplanting, making new leaves annually. Like *Encephalartos humilis,* the old leaves of *E. laevifolius* may droop and turn yellow before the new leaves emerge. Most other species may have several cycles of leaves all in good condition. Water should be withheld when the leaves turn yellow as this is a natural dormant period for the plant and watering should only be resumed when signs of new growth are noticed.

The specific name '*laevifolius*' means '*broad*' leaves.

Afforestation in its habitat has severely depleted the numbers of this attractive and hardy species.

# Plate 5. *E. laevifolius.* Stapf and Burtt Davy

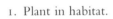

1. Plant in habitat.
2. Male cones.
3. Leaf detail. Note the yellow rhachis and the flat spread of the leaflets.
4. Female cones.

plate 6 ▶

1. Plants in habitat.
2. New leaves.
3. Leaf detail.
4. Female cones.
5. Immature male cones.
6. Male cones.

*Plate 6. E. friderici – guilielmi.* Lehm.

# Plate 6. *Encephalartos friderici – guilielmi* Lehm.

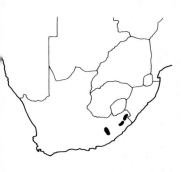

*Distribution:* EASTERN CAPE

This species grows in large numbers in the districts of Cathcart, Queenstown and as far east as Kokstad. They are usually found on mountain sides and rocky slopes. Extremes of temperature are common, with both high summer temperatures and snow and frost in winter. Summer rainfall varies from 375–500 mm.

*Stem:* The stout stems up to 4 m tall are 40 to 60 cm in diameter. Stems in excess of this height usually lean and become procumbent with age and when this happens, new plants spring from the base.

*Leaves:* The leaves are straight 1 to 1,5 m in length and are held at a 45° angle to the open brown woolly crown to accommodate the large number of cones. Median leaflets are blue-green when young and become dark green with age. They are 10 to 18 cm long and 7 to 8 mm broad, closely spaced and overlap upwards in the top third of the leaf. The lower leaflets are reduced in size but not to a series of prickles.

*Cones:* This species bears the largest number of cones in the genus. Male plants may have up to twelve cones simultaneously, while female plants with five or six large cones are not uncommon. The cones are densely woolly and lemon-yellow at first, they colour to a tawny-beige later. Male cones are 30 to 40 cm long with a diameter of 8 to 10 cm. Female cones are barrel-shaped, 25 to 30 cm long and 15 to 20 cm broad. The large number of male and female cones probably accounts for the fact that the species occurs in large numbers at each locality.

*Seeds:* Yellow-orange.

*Affinities:* Young plants of *Encephalartos friderici-guilielmi* may be confused in cultivation with *E. cycadifolius.* Even in botanical literature over the last half century confusion exists as the locality of collected specimens was often merely given as Eastern Cape.

One should look for the following features in identifying *Encephalartos friderici-guilielmi:*

1. Tall, stout stems compared with the low growing and clustering stems of *Encephalartos cycadifolius.*

2. Longer and broader median leaflets.

3. The rhachis of *Encephalartos friderici-guilielmi* is straight with the leaves held at a 45° angle to the crown, when the cones emerge the leafcrown drops to a horizontal position. The leaf crown of *Encephalartos cycadifolius* is cup-shaped at all times.

4. The crown of *Encephalartos friderici-guilielmi* is open and thickly woolly at all times, *E. cycadifolius* shows almost no wool in the crown at any stage.

5. Although both species have densely woolly cones, those of *Encephalartos friderici-guilielmi* are more numerous.

*Cultivation:* This is one of the species which is easy in cultivation and is a vigorous grower. Full sun and good drainage is essential. The many robust plants at Kirstenbosch prove that *Encephalartos friderici-guilielmi* readily adapts to different climatic conditions. Despite a winter rainfall pattern at Kirstenbosch this species produces new leaves and cones every year. It is a frost-hardy species.

The specific name honours an early patron of Botany, Frederick William, King of Prussia.

# Plate 7. *Encephalartos lanatus* Stapf and Burtt Davy

*Distribution:* TRANSVAAL

*Encephalartos lanatus* occurs in the catchment area of the Olifants River in the Middelburg, Witbank and Bronkhorstspruit districts. The species is usually found growing in sheltered valleys. The soil is deep and fertile but sandy. Summer temperatures are high and severe frost occurs in winter. Rainfall varies from 500 to 625 mm.

*Stem:* Stems are 1 to 1,5 m tall and rarely up to 2,5 m with a diameter of 25 to 30 cm. The species is easily identified by the copious amounts of wool between the leafbases of the stem.

*Leaves:* The soft green leaves are up to 1 m long. The rhachis markedly recurves in the top third of the leaf. Median leaflets are entire, 10 to 14 cm long and 6 to 8 mm broad. They are set in a tight V formation to the rachis along the entire length of the rhachis.

*Cones:* 1 to 4 densely woolly cones are borne, they are pale yellow, fading to a creamy-grey with age. Male cones are 25 to 30 cm long with a diameter of 5 to 6 cm. Female cones are larger, 25 to 35 cm long and 12 to 15 cm in diameter. Due to the regular fires in the area, new leaves and cones are borne almost every year and this regular induced coning probably accounts for the heavy plant population of all ages.

*Seeds:* Yellow. The seeds are characterized by a very thin fleshy covering.

*Affinities: Encephalartos lanatus* can be confused with *E. laevifolius* and *E. humilis*. Their distribution areas do not overlap but small plants in the garden may cause confusion.

Stem heights of mature plants in the field will differentiate the three species. *Encephalartos lanatus* falls midway between the tall, slender stemmed *E. laevifolius* and the dwarf sub-terranean *E. humilis*. The woolly leafbases of *Encephalartos lanatus* cannot be confused with the small, regular and smooth leafbases of *E. laevifolius*.

The woolly cones of *Encephalartos lanatus* are very like those of *E. humilis*, but the latter are a light brown and not pale lemon coloured like *E. lanatus*. The cones of *E. laevifolius* are more numerous than either *E. lanatus* or *E. humilis* and are not woolly at all.

The leaflets of *Encephalartos lanatus* are held in a tight V formation to the straight rhachis, *E. laevifolius* has leaflets held horizontally to the rhachis, while the leaflets of *E. humilis* are widely spaced and the rhachis is spirally twisted.

*Cultivation: Encephalartos lanatus* is difficult to re-establish in cultivation and transplanting specimens larger than 25 cm is not advised. Reasonable success has been obtained if the stem end is merely rested upon coarse sand until the new roots appear. The woolly stem requires to be misted over frequently under moist greenhouse conditions. New leaves of *Encephalartos lanatus* are sensitive to dry heat and should they appear in midsummer protection in the form of a shadecloth cover should be given until they have hardened off. This species is frost hardy.

The specific name '*lanatus*' refers to the copious amounts of wool on the stem, leaves and cones.

## Plate 7. *E. lanatus.* Stapf and Burtt Davy

1. Plants in habitat.
2. Leaf detail.
3. Female cones.
4. Male cones.

*Plate 8. E. cycadifolius.* (Jacq.) Lehm.

1. Leaf detail. Note the broad leaflets and the
   absence of wool in the crown.
2. Female cones.
3. Plant in habitat. Note the large cluster of stems.
4. Male cones.

# Plate 8. *Encephalartos cycadifolius* (Jacq.) Lehm.

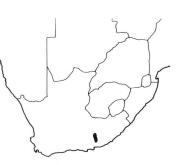

*Distribution:* EASTERN CAPE

This species is restricted to the Winterberg range in the districts of Cradock and Bedford. Plants are usually found growing on exposed northern and eastern slopes at altitudes up to 1 800 metres. Snow and frost are frequent in winter with minimum temperatures as low as −6°C. Summer rainfall varies from 625 to 800 mm.

*Stem:* The maximum stem height is less than a metre with a stem diameter of up to 30 cm. Plants sucker freely from the base and clusters of 15 to 20 stems are not uncommon in the field. Very little wool is produced in the crown at any stage.

*Leaves:* Leaves are up to 1 m long with median leaflets 9 to 12 cm long and 4 to 6 mm broad. The rhachis is slightly yellow with age and frequently has a spiral twist. Leaflets are dark green and entire. The margins of the leaflets are thickened and the undersides of the leaflets have 5 to 6 prominent veins.

*Cones:* 1 or 2 woolly yellow cones are produced from each stem. In large clusters only one or two stems will cone simultaneously. Male cones are 15 to 20 cm long and 5 to 8 cm in diameter. Female cones are 20 to 30 cm long and 16 to 18 cm in diameter.

*Seeds:* Orange-yellow coloured.

*Affinities: Encephalartos cycadifolius* is closely related to *E. ghellinckii* and *E. friderici-guilielmi* which also have woolly cones.

1. *Encephalartos cycadifolius* differs from *E. ghellinckii* in that it has no wool in the crown while the latter has a very woolly crown. (p. 62, fig. 3.)

2. The median leaflets of *Encephalartos cycadifolius* are twice as broad, and have thickened margins, those of *E. ghellinckii* are 2 to 4 mm broad with the margins rolled back.

The differences between *Encephalartos cycadifolius* and *E. friderici-guilielmi* are fully discussed under the description of the latter.

*Cultivation:* This species is difficult to establish in cultivation and a period of 4 to 5 years may elapse before new leaves appear. It rarely cones away from its habitat. Soil mixtures should be well drained and alkaline. Full sun is essential and the species is completely frost hardy.

# Plate 9. *Encephalartos humilis* Verdoorn

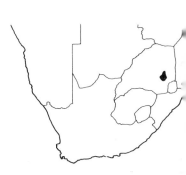

*Distribution:* EASTERN TRANSVAAL

*Encephalartos humilis* occurs in scattered groups in the mountains of the Lydenburg, Carolina and Nelspruit districts. It is frequently found growing in grassveld wedged between rocks.

*Stem:* *Encephalartos humilis* has a subterranean stem which may occasionally protrude above ground to a height of 30 cm. This dwarf species clusters freely from the rootstock and solitary specimens are rare. On lifting a stem many dormant buds may be observed. The crown is slightly woolly.

*Leaves:* The leaves are 30 to 50 cm long and the markedly yellow rhachis is both twisted and recurved giving a curly effect to the leafcrown. Median leaflets are entire, 9 to 13 cm long and 4 to 6 cm broad. New leaves are covered with fine hairs and are a soft fresh green, they turn dark green with age.

*Cones:* Both male and female plants bear a single woolly browny-grey cone. Male cones are 15 to 20 cm long and 4 to 5 cm broad. The female cone is much larger, 25 to 30 cm long and 8 to 10 cm in diameter.

*Seeds:* Bright shiny yellow and appear large in proportion to the cone.

*Affinities:* *Encephalartos humilis* is closely related to *E. lanatus* and *E. laevifolius.*

1. *Encephalartos humilis* is a subterranean species which clusters freely from the base, while *E. lanatus* and *E. laevifolius* are both stemmed plants.

2. The shorter recurved and twisted leaves of *Encephalartos humilis* cannot be confused with the straight leaves of *E. laevifolius* or the markedly recurved leaves of *E. lanatus.* The leaflets of the latter two species are much longer than those of *E. humilis.*

3. *Encephalartos humilis* has a solitary cone while *E. lanatus* and *E. laevifolius* have 1 to 5 cones per stem.

4. *Encephalartos humilis* has much less wool in the crown even when new leaves are emerging than the markedly woolly crown of *E. lanatus*, while *E. laevifolius* is noted for its complete absence of wool.

*Cultivation:* *Encephalartos humilis* does well in cultivation and requires no special treatment. Note that this species may almost be regarded as a deciduous plant. Both in habitat and cultivation the leaves of *Encephalartos humilis* die off annually just before the new leaves or cones appear. As it is a grassland species it prefers a cool root run and if grown in full sun a thick mulch will keep the soil temperature down. If grown in a container in rich compost with adequate moisture, the tendency to lose its leaves annually is lessened and several successive whorls of leaves may be retained giving a luxuriant and leafy effect.

The specific name 'humilis' meaning 'lowly' refers to the small stature of this species and its habit of nestling among boulders and long grass.

*Plate 9. E. humilis.* Verdoorn

1. Female cone showing large yellow seeds.
2. Plant in habitat.
3. Female cone.
4. Leaf detail. Note the twisted yellow rhachis.
5. Male cone.

## Plate 10. E. villosus. Lem.

1. Plant in habitat.
2. New leaves emerging.
3. Leaf detail. Note the series of prickles on the leafstalk.
4. Female cone.
5. Male cones.

# Plate 10. *Encephalartos villosus* Lem.

*Distribution:* EASTERN CAPE, NATAL, TRANSVAAL and SWAZILAND

*Encephalartos villosus* is a fairly common and widespread species which grows in the coastal and inland districts of the Eastern Cape from East London in the south to near Durban. It is also found in Zululand, the south eastern Transvaal near Pongola and extends into Swaziland. This species is usually found growing in shady moist places in low forest in temperate areas with mild winters. Rainfall is in summer and varies from 1 000 to 1 250 mm per annum.

*Stem:* This is a subterranean species which is frequently found growing in large clusters. The stem, when exposed may be 30 to 40 cm high and 30 cm in diameter.

*Leaves:* Leaves are 1,5 to 3 m long and are a glossy dark green. The rhachis recurves gracefully making it one of the most attractive foliage species. Median leaflets are 15 to 25 cm long and 1,5 to 2 cm broad with one to three teeth on both the upper and lower margins. In certain localities where very long median leaflets occur, they are usually entire. The leaflets do not overlap but are spreading and slightly recurved towards the top of the leaf. The leaflets are reduced in size to a series of prickles at the base of the leaf stalk.

*Cones:* 1 to 4 cones. The male cones are lemon-yellow, while the female cones are a deep glossy yellow. The male cone has an unpleasant odour when mature. Male cones are 60 to 70 cm long and 12 to 15 cm in diameter. Female cones are 30 to 50 cm long and 20 to 25 cm in diameter. The scale face of the female cone is flattened and overlaps the scale below. The lower edge of the scale is markedly fringed.

*Seeds:* Glossy dark red.

*Affinities: Encephalartos villosus* is closely related to *E. umbeluziensis* and may be distinguished from the latter as follows:

1. The leaflets of *E. villosus* are reduced to a series of prickles which extend to the base of the leaf stalk. On a full sized leaf, the lower 30 to 40 cm is often armed with prickles and the bottom ones may be a single 3,5 cm thorn rather than a modified leaflet. *Encephalartos umbeluziensis* has a bare petiole.

2. The leaves of *Encephalartos villosus* recurve, while those of *E. umbeluziensis* are straight.

3. Both male and female cones of *Encephalartos villosus* are larger than those of *E. umbeluziensis*. The female cones of *E. villosus* are deep yellow with the scale face fringed and overlapping the scale below. The female cones of *E. umbeluziensis* are still green at maturity and the scale face is flattened to a central facet.

*Ecotypes of Encephalartos villosus:* There is a considerable geographical variation in leaflet lengths and the number of teeth on the leaflets. Those of the Eastern Cape have short, more toothed leaflets, while those of Zululand and further north have longer leaflets which are usually entire. No distinct differences have been observed with regard to the cones and the view that these ecotypes should be given varietal status, cannot be supported.

*Hybrids of Encephalartos villosus:* Near East London, *Encephalartos villosus* and *E. altensteinii* and at Pongola Poort, *E. villosus* and *E. lebomboensis* are found growing in close proximity to one another. In both these areas numerous hybrids have been recorded with leaf and cone characters which are intermediate between the parent species. The distribution areas of *E. villosus* and *E. umbeluziensis* do not overlap but recent fieldwork points to the possibility of an intermediate species. (See Colour Plate 30, figs. 5 and 6.)

*Cultivation: Encephalartos villosus* adapts readily to cultivation and was exported in large numbers overseas at the end of the last century, where they still grace many conservatories. Under shady moist conditions in cultivation, leaves may grow to 4 m in length and the leaflet span may be 45 cm. This species should be grown in shade with ample moisture and protection from frost.

The specific name '*villosus*' refers to the dense layer of hair that covers the petiole and leaflets when the new leaves emerge.

## Plate 11. *Encephalartos umbeluziensis* R. A. Dyer

*Distribution:* SWAZILAND and MOZAMBIQUE

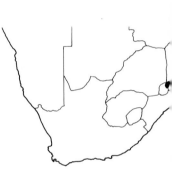

This species has a restricted distribution in Swaziland along the Umbeluzi River into Mozambique. It grows under hot and dry conditions in low scrub. Annual rainfall varies from 625 to 750 mm.

*Stem:* This is a subterranean species with a stem diameter of 20 to 25 cm. Plants are solitary and only branch when injured.

*Leaves:* The leaves are 1 to 2 m long with the rhachis straight and not recurved. The leaf colour is a glossy bright green when mature, but the leaves are covered with a silky layer of hair when young. The median leaflets are 10 to 20 cm long and 1 to 1,5 cm broad with 1 or 2 teeth on one or both margins. The leafstalk is round with no central ridge. The leaflets are reduced in size but not to prickles, leaving the lower 15 to 20 cm of the leafstalk bare to the base.

*Cones:* Cones may number up to 4 and both male and female cones are still green at maturity. Male cones are 30 cm long and 8 to 10 cm in diameter. Female cones are 25 to 30 cm long and 12 to 15 cm in diameter. The scale face is smooth and flattened to a central facet but not overlapping and fringed.

*Seeds:* Apricot-brown coloured.

*Affinities: Encephalartos umbeluziensis* is closely related to *E. villosus* but may be readily distinguished. Although both occur in Swaziland their distribution areas do not overlap. Recent field work however points to the possibility of a possible intermediate or transitional species with leaf and cone characters intermediate to those of *E. umbeluziensis* and *E. villosus* (Colour Plate 30, figs. 5 and 6).

When distinguishing between *Encephalartos umbeluziensis* and *E. villosus* the following differences should be noted:

1. The leaves of *Encephalartos umbeluziensis* are erect and spreading and do not recurve at the tips like those of *E. villosus*.

*Plate 11. E. umbeluziensis.* R. A. Dyer

1. Plant in habitat.
2. Male cones.
3. Leaf detail.
4. Female cones. Note that the cones are still green at maturity.

# Plate 12. *E. cupidus*. R. A. Dyer

1. Plant in habitat.
2. Leaf detail showing the heavily toothed leaflets.

3

1

2

4

3. Male cones.
4. Female cone.

2. The rhachis of *Encephalartos umbeluziensis* is round and smooth, the leaflets though reduced in size, do not end in a series of prickles and the lower 15 to 20 cm of the leafstalk is bare.

3. The female cone scales of *Encephalartos umbeluziensis* are flattened to a central facet, the female cone scales of *E. villosus* are fringed and overlap the scale below.

4. The cones of *Encephalartos umbeluziensis* are still green at maturity and the seeds are apricot-brown, the cones of *E. villosus* are a deep yellow-orange at maturity and the seeds are dark red.

5. When new leaves emerge, very little wool is produced in the crown of *Encephalartos umbeluziensis*, the leaves and leafstalk of *E. villosus* are covered in thick white wool which persists until the leaves have reached their full length.

*Cultivation:* This species grows well in cultivation. Unlike *E. villosus* the leaves will not burn if grown in full sun, but it can only be considered semi-hardy.

The specific name refers to the type locality near the Umbeluzi River.

# Plate 12. *Encephalartos cupidus* R. A. Dyer

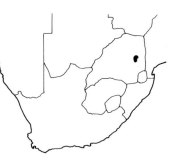

*Distribution:* TRANSVAAL

*Encephalartos cupidus* grows in the Pilgrims Rest district of the Eastern Transvaal. It is frequently found growing between boulders in open grassland. The rainfall varies from 625 to 750 mm per annum.

*Stem:* This is a dwarf-growing species and the stems of mature plants are seldom more than 15 cm above the ground. It suckers freely from the base and clusters of ten to twelve heads are not uncommon.

*Leaves:* The leaves are up to 1 m long and a glaucous blue-green in colour. The rhachis is straight and the tip of the leaf is upturned. The leaves are held almost horizontally to the crown making this a most decorative plant. The median leaflets are 10 to 15 cm long and 10 to 12 mm broad. The leaflets are heavily toothed on both margins. The leaflets are reduced in size to not more than two or three prickles at the base of the leafstalk.

*Cones:* The cones are solitary and a bright apple-green even at maturity. The male cones are 18 to 20 cm in length and 5 to 8 cm in diameter. The female cones are 18 to 20 cm long and 12 to 14 cm in diameter.

*Seeds:* Apricot coloured.

*Affinities:* The nearest relative to *Encephalartos cupidus* is *E. munchii*, a species from Mozambique. The leafcolour of the latter is however slightly greener and it has much larger cones. The leaflets of *Encephalartos cupidus* are held in a tight V formation to the rhachis, while those of *E. munchii* are held almost horizontally to the rhachis.

In appearance *Encephalartos cupidus* often resembles a juvenile plant of *E. eugene-maraisii*. The leaflets of *Encephalartos cupidus* are heavily toothed while those of juvenile plants of *E. eugene-maraisii* will only occasionally have one tooth on the lower margin.

*Cultivation:* *Encephalartos cupidus* grows well in cultivation and the leaves often grow to 1,5 m in length. Profuse suckering from the base is characteristic of garden grown plants. Full sun and good drainage is essential. This is a frosthardy species.

The specific name *'cupidus'* means *'that which is desirable'*.


## Plate 13. *Encephalartos eugene-maraisii* Verdoorn

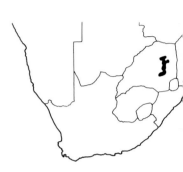

*Distribution:* TRANSVAAL

Various forms of this species occur in widely separated parts of the Transvaal. These areas are Middelburg, the Waterberg, the Wolkberg and much further east in the Mica district. They all experience very cold winters and the rainfall varies from 625 to 750 mm in the first two localities to over 1 250 mm in the Wolkberg.

The following description is based on the type plants found in the Waterberg area:

*Stem:* Stem heights seldom exceed 2,5 m when upright and if taller, the plants are usually procumbent. The diameter of the stem with its small regular leafbases is 30 to 45 cm.

*Leaves:* The leaves are 1 to 1,5 m long and a silver-blue colour. The rhachis is straight but the top third of the leafstalk curves upwards. The leaves are spreading and held almost horizontally to the crown. The median leaflets are 15 to 20 cm long and 1,5 cm broad. The margins are usually entire but may have one tooth on the lower margin. The leaflets are reduced in size to no more than one prickle, leaving the lower 15 cm of the leafstalk bare to the base.

*Cones:* Up to 8 male cones and 6 female cones have been recorded. The cones are greeny-grey overlaid with a dense layer of maroon hair giving a generally dark brown-red appearance to the cones. Male cones are 20 to 40 cm long and 6 to 8 cm broad and have an unpleasant odour when mature. The female cones are 30 to 50 cm long and 16 to 20 cm broad.

*Seeds:* Light brown (known as Wildedadels (Wild Dates) locally).

*Affinities:* *Encephalartos eugene-maraisii* is closely related to the Eastern Cape species *E. lehmannii* which it resembles:

1. *Encephalartos eugene-maraisii* is a taller and more robust plant, *E. lehmannii* seldom exceeds 1,5 metres in height.

2. *Encephalartos eugene-maraisii* has leaves with a distinct upward curve to the tips, those of *E. lehmannii* recurve at the tips.

3. *Encephalartos eugene-maraisii* lacks the distinct 'collar' at the base of the leafstalk (Diagram p. 1) which is prominent and distinct in *E. lehmannii*.

*Geographical differences:* Distinct differences in leaves, stems and cones are constant when specimens from various localities are examined and the species is at present under review, with one possible new species a consideration. A full discussion of these geographical forms appears on page 40.

*Cultivation:* This species grows well in cultivation and is frosthardy. It should be grown in full sun to preserve the blue colour of the leaves.

The specific name honours Eugene Marais, the poet and naturalist, who brought the plant to the notice of his niece Dr Inez Verdoorn.

*Plate 13. E. eugene-maraisii.* Verdoorn

1. Plant in habitat (Middelburg form).
2. Leaf detail showing the marked upcurved rhachis of the Waterberg form.
3. Female cones (Waterberg form).
4. Male cones (Waterberg form).

# Plate 14. E. lehmannii. Lehm.

1. Male cone.
2. Plant in habitat.
3. Female cone.
4. Leaf detail. Note that the leaflets are well spaced and not overlapping. Their attachment to the rhachis is horizontal.

# Plate 14. *Encephalartos lehmannii* Lehm.

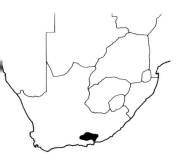

*Distribution:* EASTERN CAPE

The area in which *Encephalartos lehmannii* occurs extends from the Karroo districts of Pearston and Bedford westwards through Uitenhage, Steytlerville to near Willowmore. This species grows mainly on sandstone hills in areas of Karroo scrub and *Euphorbia*. Summer rainfall is low, seldom exceeding 350 mm with prolonged periodic droughts. Winters are severe.

*Stem:* This species has a short sturdy stem up to 1,5 m and rarely reaches 2 m, with a diameter of 25 to 45 cm. The leafbases are large and at the crown a distinct yellow collar is visible where the leafstalk joins the stem.

*Leaves:* The 1 to 1,5 m long leaves recurve slightly at the tips. Median leaflets are 12 to 18 cm long and 1,5 to 2 cm broad. They are entire with an occasional tooth on the lower margin. Their attachment to the rhachis is horizontal to the axis and they do not overlap in the top third but are well spaced. The leaves are a glaucous-blue, when young but may turn green with age.

*Cones:* Both male and female plants bear solitary cones which are blackish-red over green, this colour effect is due to the dense layer of fine black hair which covers the terminal facet. Male cones are 25 to 35 cm long and 8 to 10 cm in diameter. Female cones are 45 to 50 cm long and 25 cm in diameter, at maturity they shed the layer of fine hair and appear more green than brown. The scale face is relatively smooth.

*Seeds:* Bright red and large.

*Affinities:* A close relationship exists between *Encephalartos lehmannii*, *E. princeps*, *E. trispinosus* and *E. horridus*. *Encephalartos lehmannii* most closely resembles *E. princeps* and may be distinguished as follows:

1. *Encephalartos lehmannii* has shorter stems, seldom exceeding 1,5 m while *E. princeps* is a taller growing more robust species.

2. The leaflets of *Encephalartos lehmannii* are well spaced and do not overlap in the top third of the leaf as do those of *E. princeps*.

3. *Encephalartos lehmannii* has solitary cones which are blackish-red over green and the female cones have a relatively smooth terminal facet while those of *E. princeps* may be up to three in number and are a dull olive-green with a warty wrinkled terminal facet to the female cone scales.

4. The distribution areas of these two species do not overlap and no confusion exists in the field. Plants in cultivation can be positively identified as *Encephalartos lehmannii* by the well spaced leaflets and the leafbases which are much larger than those of *E. princeps*.

*Cultivation:* This is an easy and extremely hardy species which requires full sun and a neutral to alkaline soil. If grown in shade and with too much moisture the leaves will lose their metallic blue colour and become green.

This species was named after Professor J. G. C. Lehmann who in 1834 published a work on cycads and established the separate genus of *Encephalartos*.

# Plate 15. *Encephalartos princeps* R. A. Dyer

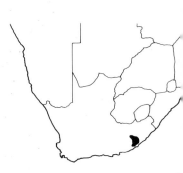

*Distribution:* EASTERN CAPE

*Encephalartos princeps* grows on dolerite cliffs in the districts Queenstown, Cathcart, Komgha and Butterworth in the catchment area of the Kei River. Summers are hot and winters are severe. The annual rainfall seldom exceeds 450 to 500 mm.

*Stems:* Stems may reach a height of 4 m or more with a diameter of 30 to 40 cm. Very tall stems become procumbent and recline with age and suckers then appear from the base.

*Leaves:* The leaves are 1 to 1,3 metres in length and the tip of the rhachis is curved downwards. The median leaflets are usually entire, 15 cm long and 1,5 cm broad. When young the leaves are a silvery-blue but they may become a dull green with age and contrast markedly with the new leaves. The leaflets are well spaced in the lower half but become crowded and closely overlap upwards in the top half.

*Cones:* 1 to 3 cones are borne and are a dull olive-green. Male cones are 20 to 25 cm long and 8 to 10 cm in diameter. Female cones are 30 to 40 cm long and 20 to 25 cm in diameter. The terminal facet of the female cone scales protrudes and has a coarse, warty appearance.

*Seeds:* Bright red.

*Affinities:* Encephalartos princeps was only separated as a species from *E. lehmannii* in 1965. The distinction is based on the following differences.

1. The distribution area of *Encephalartos princeps* is limited to the catchment area of the Kei River, while *E. lehmannii* occurs further west in the catchment of the Sundays and Groot River valleys.

2. *Encephalartos princeps* occurs on dolerite outcrops whereas *E. lehmannii* favours sedimentary sandstone formations.

3. *Encephalartos princeps* is a taller more robust species than *E. lehmannii* which seldom exceeds 1,5 m.

4. The leaflets of *Encephalartos princeps* are densely spaced and overlap closely upwards in the top third of the leaf.

5. The cones of *Encephalartos princeps* are olive-green in colour and may number up to three, while *E. lehmannii* has a solitary blackish-red to green cone.

*Cultivation:* This is an extremely hardy and attractive species which must have full sun and good drainage. Plants in cultivation retain the blue colour of the leaves longer than those growing in their natural habitat.

The specific name '*princeps*' means '*the first*' and this was chosen by Dr R. A. Dyer because he considered that *Encephalartos princeps* had evolved earlier in the evolutionary series than the rest of the species in the group which includes *E. lehmannii*, *E. horridus* and *E. trispinosus*.

*Plate 15. E. princeps.* R. A. Dyer

1. Plant in habitat.
2. Female cones. Note how the cone scales spiral.

1

2

3. Leaf detail. Note that the leaflets are closely spaced and overlap. Their attachment to the rhachis is at an angle and not horizontally.
4. Male cones.

3

4

## Plate 16. *E. longifolius.* (Jacq.) Lehm.

1

2

1. Male cones.
2. Plant in habitat.
3. Leaf detail. Note the yellow rhachis.
4. Female cone.

3

4

# Plate 16. *Encephalartos longifolius* (Jacq.) Lehm.

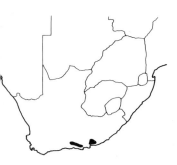

*Distribution:* EASTERN CAPE

This is the first species of cycad that Thunberg encountered in his travels. It grows from Joubertina eastwards through the districts of Humansdorp, Uitenhage to Somerset East. On the Zuurberge it grows on mountain slopes in exposed grassland habitats. At Van Stadens Nature Reserve it grows among macchia vegetation in sourveld with a PH value of 5,4 and a winter rainfall of 1 250 mm. Further north at Paardepoort the rainfall drops to 350 to 400 mm and it is associated with Karroo scrub.

*Stem:* Encephalartos longifolius has tall, heavy stems up to 4 m with a diameter of 30 to 45 cm. The base of the stem is often so compressed due to the weight of the trunk, that the leaf bases are no longer visible.

*Leaves:* The leaves are 1 to 2 metres long and the pale yellow rhachis arches gracefully. The leaves are a dark glossy green but those in the drier localities are more glaucous and blue. Median leaflets are up to 20 cm long and 2 to 3 cm broad, usually entire but occasionally with one or two teeth on the lower margin. Leaflets overlap upwards towards the top of the leaf.

*Cones:* 1 to 3 greenish-brown cones are borne. The cones of *Encephalartos longifolius* are the largest in the genus with the male cones 40 to 60 cm long and 15 to 20 cm in diameter. Female cones are 60 cm long and 40 cm in diameter and may weigh up to 30 kg. (Chamberlain in *The Living Cycad* records that a solitary cone weighed 40 kg.)

*Seeds:* Bright red.

*Affinities:* Its nearest related species is *Encephalartos altensteinii* but as their distribution areas do not overlap, there should be no confusion in the field. *Encephalartos longifolius* is an inland species associated with Table Mountain sandstone whereas *E. altensteinii* is found mainly in the coastal bush further to the east. Plants in cultivation may cause confusion.

1. *Encephalartos longifolius* leaves are a much darker green with a distinct bloom, the leaves of *E. altensteinii* are a bright, fresh green.

2. The leaflets of *Encephalartos longifolius* overlap markedly in the top third of the leaf and the arching of the rhachis gives a graceful curve to the leaf. The leaflets of *E. altensteinii* do not overlap markedly and the rhachis is straight and held at a 45° angle to the crown.

3. The cones of *Encephalartos longifolius* are smooth and dark olive-green, while those of *E. altensteinii* are golden-yellow and slightly felted and tomentose.

*Hybrids of Encephalartos longifolius:* In certain localities where they occur together *Encephalartos longifolius* hybridises readily with *E. horridus* and leaf and cone characters intermediate to both parents are present. (Colour Plate 30, figs. 3 and 4.)

*Cultivation:* Encephalartos longifolius does well in cultivation and prefers a slightly acid soil mixture with ample moisture. This species is semi-hardy.

The specific name '*longifolius*' means '*long leaves*' and this is one of the most attractive foliage species.

# Plate 17. *Encephalartos altensteinii* Lehm.

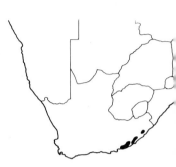

*Distribution*: EASTERN CAPE

*Encephalartos altensteinii* occurs in the coastal bush from Alexandria eastwards through the districts of King William's Town, East London and Umtata to near the Natal border. Annual rainfall varies from 875 to 1 000 mm.

*Stem*: This is one of the taller growing species with stems of 4 to 5 m and occasionally up to 7 m when growing in heavy shade. The diameter of the stem is 25 to 35 cm. Due to the fact that they grow in sheltered positions in the coastal bush they are not subject to wind sway and seldom lean but remain upright.

*Leaves*: Leaves are 1 to 2 m long with a straight rhachis. In heavy shade the leaves are sometimes recurved. The median leaflets are 15 cm long and 2,5 cm broad and a fresh green colour. Leaflets may have 1 to 3 teeth on either margin with younger plants more toothed than older ones. The leaflets are reduced in size but not to a series of prickles and the lower 15 to 20 cm of the leafstalk is bare.

*Cones*: Both male and female plants may have 1 to 5 golden-yellow cones. Male cones are 40 to 50 cm long and 12 to 15 cm in diameter. Female cones are 40 to 55 cm long and 25 to 30 cm in diameter. The scale face of the female cones is deeply wrinkled and slightly felted and tomentose.

*Seeds*: Bright shiny red.

*Affinities*: *Encephalartos altensteinii* is closely related to *E. natalensis*, in fact, many authorities regard *E. lebomboensis*, *E. natalensis* and *E. altensteinii* as geographical variations of one species.

*Encephalartos altensteinii* may be distinguished as follows from *E. natalensis*:

1. *Encephalartos altensteinii* lacks the series of prickles at the base of the leafstalk and this may be regarded as a fairly constant distinguishing feature between it and *E. natalensis*.

2. *Encephalartos altensteinii* shows no wool in the crown when new leaves emerge whereas *E. natalensis* produces copious amounts of wool prior to new leaves or cones appearing.

*Hybrids of Encephalartos altensteinii*: Within the distribution area of *Encephalartos altensteinii*, four other species also occur and natural hybridization has taken place. The following hybrids have been recorded:

*E. altensteinii* × *E. villosus*
*E. altensteinii* × *E. trispinosus*
*E. altensteinii* × *E. arenarius*
*E. altensteinii* × *E. latifrons*

(See Colour Plate 30, fig. 2.)

*Cultivation*: *Encephalartos altensteinii* grows well in cultivation and may be grown either in full sun or in shade. The species is semi-hardy.

The specific name honours a German chancellor of the 19th Century.

*Plate 17. E. altensteinii.* Lehm.

4      1      2

1. Female cones.
2. Male cones.
3. Plant in habitat.
4. Leaf detail. Note the absence of prickles on
   the petioles

3      4

*Plate 18. E. lebomboensis.* Verdoorn

1. Plants growing on cliff faces.
2. Leaf detail. Note the marked overlapping of the leaflets and pattern formed by the teeth on the margins.
3. Male cone.
4. Female cone.
5. Plants growing in a bush group habitat.

# Plate 18. *Encephalartos lebomboensis* Verdoorn

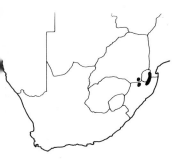

*Distribution:* NATAL, SWAZILAND, TRANSVAAL and MOZAMBIQUE
*Encephalartos lebomboensis* grows on the cliff faces and in the kloofs of the Lebombo Mountain Range in the districts of Ubombo, Ingwavuma, Paulpietersburg in Natal, Piet Retief in the Transvaal, Stegi in Swaziland and into Mozambique. The rainfall in summer varies from 625 to 750 mm.

*Stem:* The stems of this species are up to 4 m tall and 25 to 30 cm in diameter. The stems are very characteristic with mixed small and large leafbases giving a 'patchwork' effect, this reflects periods when prolonged droughts alternated with very wet seasons.

*Leaves:* The leaves are 1 to 1,5 m long and a fresh bright green colour. The rhachis is usually straight but may be recurved at the tip. The median leaflets are narrow and only 1,5 cm broad, they are 12 to 18 cm in length. The leaflets are rarely without teeth and usually have a regular pattern of 2 to 4 teeth on both margins. The leaflets are closely spaced and overlap downwards. (Diagram p. 18.) The leaflets are reduced to a series of prickles which extend to the base of the leafstalk.

*Cones:* 1 to 3 golden-yellow cones are borne. The male cones are up to 45 cm long and 12 to 15 cm in diameter. The female cones are 40 to 45 cm long and 25 to 30 cm in diameter. The scale faces of the female cones are relatively smooth and less woolly than those of *E. natalensis.*

*Seeds:* Bright red.

*Affinities: Encephalartos lebomboensis* is closely related to *E. natalensis* and may be distinguished as follows:

1. The leaflets of *Encephalartos lebomboensis* are shorter and narrower than those of *E. natalensis.* They are fairly heavily toothed in a regular pattern which is accentuated by the close overlapping of the leaflets. *Encephalartos natalensis* has broader and more widely spaced leaflets which seldom overlap.

2. The lower portion of the leafstalk of *Encephalartos lebomboensis* is densely prickled right to the base, whereas *E. natalensis* has 7 to 10 cm of petiole with no prickles.

3. The female cone scales of *Encephalartos lebomboensis* are relatively smooth and flat while those of *E. natalensis* are prominently wrinkled and tomentose.

Certain geographical differences within the species occur and plants in some localities do not have the characteristic prickles to the base of the leafstalk. Confusion with *Encephalartos altensteinii* need not occur as the leaflets of these forms of *E. lebomboensis* are shorter and narrower than those of *E. altensteinii.*

Hybrids between *Encephalartos lebomboensis* and *E. villosus* occur in the vicinity of the Pongola River and leaf and cone characters are intermediate between the parent species.

*Cultivation: Encephalartos lebomboensis* adapts readily to cultivation and it is the most common species in collections. Over 6 000 mature plants were rescued by Operation Wildflower when the J. G. Strijdom Dam was built. It should be grown in full sun and is semi-hardy. The specific name refers to the type locality, the Lebombo Mountains.

# Plate 19. *Encephalartos natalensis* Dyer and Verdoorn

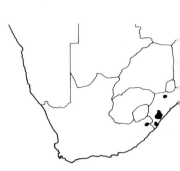

*Distribution:* NATAL

This is an inland species which grows on rocky outcrops from the Southern Natal border in the districts of Port Shepstone, Eston, Howick and Kranskop northwards to Vryheid.

*Stem:* This is a tall growing species with stems up to 4 m and occasionally up to 6 m. The stem diameter is 25 to 40 cm and the stems are usually erect, only becoming procumbent when other stems emerge from the same base. The crown will show copious amounts of wool when new leaves or cones emerge.

*Leaves:* The leaves are 1,5 to 3 m long with a straight rhachis. The median leaflets are 15 to 25 cm long and 2,5 to 4 cm broad. The margins are usually entire but may have one to four teeth on one or both margins. Young plants are usually more toothed than older plants. The leaflets are reduced to a series of prickles towards the base of the leafstalk. The leaf colour is a deep glossy green.

*Cones:* They may have up to five deep golden-yellow cones. Male cones are paler in colour, 45 to 50 cm long and 10 to 12 cm in diameter. Female cones are 50 to 60 cm long and 25 to 30 cm in diameter. The female cone scales are deeply wrinkled and both male and female cones are woolly at first, gradually losing this wool with age.

*Seeds:* Bright orange-red.

*Affinities: Encephalartos natalensis* is closely related to *E. lembomboensis, E. altensteinii* and *E. woodii.* The differences between *Encephalartos natalensis* and *E. altensteinii* and *E. lebomboensis* have already been discussed under the descriptions of the latter two species. *Encephalartos natalensis* may be distinguished from *E. woodii* as follows:

1. *Encephalartos natalensis* has straight leaves held at a 45° angle to the crown, the leaves of *E. woodii* arch gracefully to form a heavy umbrella shaped canopy.

2. The median leaflets of *Encephalartos natalensis* are 2,5 to 4 cm broad, the margins are usually entire or they may have one to four teeth on one or both margins. The median and the lower leaflets of *E. woodii* are much broader, 5 to 6 cm wide and have a characteristic pattern of lobes. (See Diagram p. 46.)

*Geographical forms:* Several geographical differences exist within the concept of *Encephalartos natalensis* Dyer and Verdoorn, e.g. the broad leaved form from the Kranskop area, and the woolly crowned form from Vryheid. The cones however do not show any marked differences and the separation of these ecotypes as varietal forms or even species, does not appear to be justified.

*Cultivation:* This is an easily grown species which does well in cultivation. Three-year-old seedlings are already garden worthy with leaves of 1 m in length.

*Encephalartos natalensis* requires ample moisture and a rich soil mixture. Although this is an inland species, it has proved to be sensitive to frost, particularly if new leaves appear in late summer.

The specific name means *'from Natal'*.

*Plate 19. E. natalensis.* Dyer and Verdoorn

1. Plant in habitat.
2. Leaf detail.
3. Female cones.
4. Male cones.

*Plate 20. E. woodii.* Sander

1

2

3

4

1. Plant in the Durban Botanic Gardens.
2. Immature male cones.
3. Leaf detail. Note the characteristic pattern of lobes on the top margin of the leaflet.
4. Spent male cones.

# Plate 20. *Encephalartos woodii* Sander

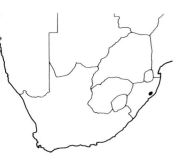

*Distribution:* NATAL

Only one clump of male plants was found in the Ngoye forest in the Mtunzini district in 1895. No female plant is known to exist and the species may be regarded as extinct in nature.

*Stem:* The stem height of the tallest plant in cultivation is 6 m. The stem at the base is 90 cm in diameter narrowing to 60 cm at the crown. This broadening of the stem at the base into a form of buttress is unique to *Encephalartos woodii*. At ground level the leafbases are so compressed that they have a smooth trunk-like appearance. One of the plants in cultivation branches at the crown. Many dormant buds may be observed along the entire length of the stem, a characteristic it shares with *Encephalartos transvenosus* and *E. paucidentatus*.

*Leaves:* The leaves are 2 to 2,5 m long with a gracefully arching rhachis which gives the plant an umbrella shaped canopy of leaves. The median leaflets of mature plants are 20 cm long, 4 cm broad and the margins are often entire. The leaflets are reduced in size towards the base and end in a series of prickles. The leaflets of young suckers differ markedly from those of mature plants. The median leaflets are shorter and broader and have a characteristic pattern of lobes. (See Diagram p. 46.) The leaf colour is a dark glossy green.

*Cones:* Up to six male cones have been recorded. They are bright orange, 40 to 90 cm in length and occasionally up to 1,2 m. The diameter varies from 15 to 20 cm.

*Affinities: Encephalartos woodii* is closely related to *E. natalensis* and some authorities regard it as a mutation within the concept of *E. natalensis* Dyer and Verdoorn.

1. *Encephalartos woodii* is distinguished from *E. natalensis* by the spreading canopy of arching leaves even in young plants.

2. The median leaflets of *Encephalartos woodii*, particularly those of young suckers are 5 to 6 cm broad and have a characteristic pattern of lobes. The leaflets of *E. natalensis* are only 2,5 to 4 cm broad and are usually entire but may have one or two teeth on one or both margins.

3. The male cones of *Encephalartos woodii* are a rich bright orange colour compared to the pale yellow male cones of *E. natalensis*.

*Cultivation: Encephalartos woodii* has proved to be one of the most vigorous growing species in cultivation. Not only does it make numerous suckers but new leaves are formed every year and the stem heights show a much faster rate of growth than any other species. Ample moisture is required and a rich soil mixture. In hot and dry inland areas light shade is necessary to prevent the leaves burning.

The specific name honours Medley Wood, Director of the Natal Government Herbarium, who found the only specimen in 1895.

# Plate 21. *Encephalartos transvenosus* Stapf and Burtt Davy

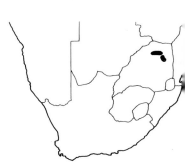

*Distribution:* TRANSVAAL

This species occurs in the Soutpansberg and the Letaba districts of the Northern Transvaal. At Modjadji's Kraal in the Duiwelskloof district, the Rain Queens of the Lovedu have protected the species for many generations. Today the dense forest of cycads on the hills below her home is one of the most unique botanical features in South Africa. Summer mists are frequent in this area and the rainfall is in excess of 1 500 mm per annum. Summers are cool and humid and no frost occurs.

*Stem:* This is the tallest growing species with stems of 12 to 13 m at Modjadji's Kraal but usually 5 to 8 m. The stem diameter is 40 to 45 cm. A feature of *Encephalartos transvenosus* is that the stem usually shows many dormant buds along its entire length, a characteristic it shares with *E. woodii* and *E. paucidentatus.*

*Leaves:* The leaves are 1,5 to 2,5 m long with a markedly yellow rhachis. The leaves are a glossy dark green. The median leaflets are 16 to 25 cm long and 2,5 to 4,5 cm broad. The leaflets are reduced in size towards the base of the leafstalk. A distinguishing feature is that the leaflets are not held horizontally to the rhachis, but that they are reflexed from the rhachis. They are closely spaced and overlap upwards. They are usually toothed on both the upper and lower margins.

*Cones:* The cones which may number up to four are golden-brown and slightly woolly at first. Male cones are 30 to 40 cm long and 13 to 15 cm in diameter. The female cones are very large and heavy, 50 to 80 cm long and 20 to 30 cm in diameter and may weigh up to 34 kg.

*Seeds:* Bright orange-red.

*Affinities:* Although the leaflets of both *Encephalartos transvenosus* and *E. paucidentatus* are reflexed from the rhachis, the two species may easily be distinguished as follows:

1. The leaflets of *Encephalartos transvenosus* are broader and overlap markedly in the top half of the leaf, those of *E. paucidentatus* are not as closely spaced.

2. The leaflets of *Encephalartos transvenosus* when held up to the light will show a network of fine veins between the main parallel veins, whereas *E. paucidentatus* has about thirty conspicuously raised veins on the lower surface of the leaf.

*Cultivation:* This is a strikingly handsome species in cultivation and should be given ample moisture and some shade. In its habitat summers are cool and humid and when grown in drier areas in full sun, the leaves are often scorched. New leaves which emerge in late summer may be damaged by frost and protection against frost and cold winds is necessary. Seedlings grow very rapidly and four- to five-year-old plants are already garden worthy with 1 m long leaves.

The specific name '*transvenosus*' refers to the fine network of veins which can be seen when a leaflet is held against the light.

*Plate 21. E. transvenosus.* Stapf and Burtt Davy

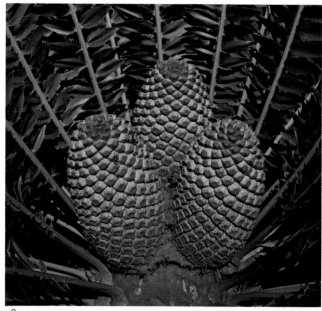

1. Plants in habitat at Modjadji's Kraal.
2. New leaves emerging immediately after coning.
3. Female cones.
4. Male cones.
5. Leaf detail. Note how the leaflets overlap and
   reflex from the rhachis.

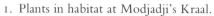

*Plate 22. E. paucidentatus.* Stapf and Burtt Davy

1. Female cones.
2. Leaf detail. Note that the leaflets are reflexed from the rhachis but do not overlap.
3. Plant in habitat.
4. Male cones.

# Plate 22. *Encephalartos paucidentatus* Stapf and Burtt Davy

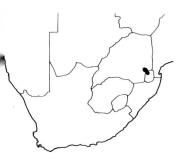

*Distribution:* EASTERN TRANSVAAL and SWAZILAND

*Encephalartos paucidentatus* has a limited distribution in the mountains and forests in the Barberton district of the Transvaal and the Piggs Peak area of Swaziland. The species is found at altitudes up to 1 800 metres in areas with an annual rainfall of 1 250 to 1 500 mm.

*Stem:* Stems are up to 6 m tall and 40 to 70 cm in diameter with large leafbases.

*Leaves:* Leaves are 1,5 to 2,5 m long and a dark glossy green. The rhachis is straight, markedly yellow and the leaf crown is graceful and spreading. The median leaflets are 15 to 25 cm long and 2 to 3,5 cm broad with one or more teeth on both margins. A distinctive feature is the ± thirty prominent veins on the lower surface of the leaflets. The leaflets are reflexed from the rhachis.

*Cones:* 1 to 5 golden-brown cones are borne. They are very woolly at first and become less so at maturity. Male cones are 40 to 60 cm long and 12 to 15 cm in diameter. Female cones are 35 to 50 cm in length and 20 to 25 cm broad. The female cone scales and the terminal facets are deeply furrowed.

*Seeds:* Bright red.

*Affinities: Encephalartos paucidentatus* is closely related to *E. transvenosus* and *E. heenanii.* The distribution areas of *Encephalartos paucidentatus* and *E. transvenosus* do not overlap and confusion between these two species is not possible in the field, however *E. paucidentatus* and *E. heenanii* grow within a kilometre of one another in the Piggs Peak area and difficulty may be experienced in distinguishing between them.

The differences between *Encephalartos paucidentatus* and *E. transvenosus* are fully discussed under the description of the latter. *Encephalartos paucidentatus* may be distinguished from *E. heenanii* as follows:

1. *Encephalartos paucidentatus* is a tall species with a graceful spreading crown, the leaves may be 1,5 to 2,5 m long while *E. heenanii* leaves are seldom longer than 1 to 1,2 m and are gently curved giving a cup-shaped outline to the leaf crown.

2. The leaves of *Encephalartos paucidentatus* are dark green and glossy at maturity, having one or more teeth on both margins and are seldom entire. Those of *E. heenanii* are a pale light green and markedly woolly at all times, they are entire and only in juvenile forms will one or two teeth be observed.

*Cultivation: Encephalartos paucidentatus* is a difficult species to re-establish in cultivation due to its very specific habitat conditions. After transplanting several years may elapse before new leaves emerge and care should be taken to retain as many of the roots as possible. As it is a forest species, shade and ample moisture are essential. Sunburn and frost damage may occur if conditions are too far removed from those of its habitat.

The specific name '*paucidentatus*' means '*with few teeth*'.

## Plate 23. *Encephalartos heenanii* R. A. Dyer

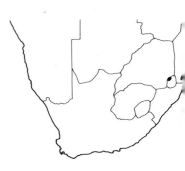

*Distribution:* TRANSVAAL and SWAZILAND

This species occurs on the mountains on the border between the Transvaal and Swaziland in the Piggs Peak and Havelock area. They grow at altitudes of 1 800 m in the protea belt in sheltered kloofs. The rainfall is mainly in summer and averages 1 250 mm per annum.

*Stem:* The stems are up to 3 m tall with a diameter of 25 to 35 cm. A feature of this species is the copious quantities of golden-brown wool present, not only are the leaves and cones woolly but also the entire length of the stem when leaves and cones emerge. The species could well have been named *Encephalartos tomentosus* had a descriptive epithet been thought desirable.

*Leaves:* The leaves are 1 to 1,25 m long. The rhachis curves gently giving a marked cup-shaped outline to the leaf crown. The leaves are a pale silvery-green and woolly even at maturity. The median leaflets are 12 to 15 cm long and 1,5 to 2 cm broad. The margins are entire except that very rarely one or two teeth may be observed on the leaves of juvenile plants. The leaflets are well spaced and reflexed from the rhachis.

*Cones:* Encephalartos heenanii is unique among the South African cycads in that the male and female cones are very similar in size and shape and cannot be readily distinguished on the plant. Only when they are removed does the weight and internal structures make identification possible. Up to three cones occur which are copiously covered with long golden-brown hair. The male cones are 27 to 30 cm long and 15 to 17 cm broad. The female cones are 23 to 30 cm long and 17 to 18 cm in diameter. Most male cones will elongate at maturity in order to release the pollen, but the male cones of *Encephalartos heenanii* remain broad and egg-shaped.

*Affinities:* Encephalartos heenanii is closely related to E. paucidentatus and may be distinguished as follows:

1. *Encephalartos heenanii* is a medium sized plant which does not grow as tall as *E. paucidentatus* a species that grows to a height of up to 6 m.

2. The leaves of *Encephalartos heenanii* are a pale silvery-green and usually entire while *E. paucidentatus* has glossy dark green leaves and one or two teeth on the margins. The leaflets of the latter are closely overlapping while those of *Encephalartos heenanii* are more widely spaced.

3. The leaves, stem and cones of *Encephalartos heenanii* are markedly woolly at all times, *E. paucidentatus* will show a little wool in the crown when the new leaves or cones emerge but soon loses this hair.

4. The leafcrown of *Encephalartos heenanii* has a distinct cup-shaped outline, while the 2,5 m long leaves of *E. paucidentatus* are straight and spreading.

*Cultivation:* It is a sad commentary that a cycad as recently discovered as 1969 should already be so well represented in collections, both here and abroad. One trusts that the avarice of collectors, will not lead to its disappearance from its natural habitat, which on the basis of existing field records, is extremely restricted.

The specific name honours Mr Denis Heenan who brought this new species to the notice of the Botanical Research Institute.

*Plate 23. E. heenanii.* R. A. Dyer

1. The leaf crown is cup-shaped and the leaflets
   are reflexed from the rhachis.
2. Crown and leaf detail. Note the copious
   amounts of wool in the crown and the petioles
   and leaves.
3. Leaf detail.
4. Female cone showing seeds.
5. Immature male cone.

*Plate 24. E. horridus.* (Jacq.) Lehm.

1. Leaf detail.
2. Plant in habitat.
3. Male cone.
4. Female cone.

# Plate 24. *Encephalartos horridus* (Jacq.) Lehm.

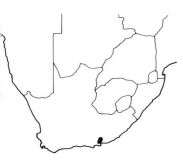

*Distribution:* EASTERN CAPE

This species occurs in the Uitenhage and Port Elizabeth districts where it may be found growing among the Karroo scrub vegetation. Plants which grow in the quartzite hills beyond Port Elizabeth in infertile sourveld are much smaller in stature than those growing in the fertile but dry Uitenhage area. No differences in leaf and cone characters, except size, exist and under cultivation this dwarf nature may disappear. The rainfall varies from 450 to 550 mm per annum.

*Stem:* This is a low growing species and the stem when exposed seldom exceeds 50 cm. It suckers freely from the base and large clusters may be observed in the field.

*Leaves:* The leaves are up to 1 m in length with the top third sharply recurved. The leaves are an intense glaucous blue. The median leaflets are 10 cm long and 2,5 cm to 4 cm broad with two to three prominent lobes which may be up to 4 cm in length. See Diagram on page 45. These lobes are twisted out of the plane of the leaflet and in the top third of the leaf where the leaflets are closely spaced, they will form a regular and even pattern.

*Cones:* The cones are solitary and a brownish-red over green due to the dense layer of fine hair on the surface of the cone scale. Male cones are 20 to 40 cm long and 6 to 12 cm in diameter. Female cones are 25 to 40 cm long and 15 to 20 cm in diameter. In cultivation male plants will often cone several times a year in succession.

*Seeds:* Pale red.

*Affinities:* A close relationship exists between *Encephalartos horridus* and *E. trispinosus*. The following differences help to distinguish them:

1. No confusion should exist in the field as *Encephalartos horridus* is restricted to the districts of Port Elizabeth and Uitenhage whereas *E. trispinosus* occurs much further east in the catchment of the Bushman's River and Fish River.

2. The leaves of *Encephalartos horridus* are an intense blue and the rhachis recurves sharply in the top third, the leaves of *E. trispinosus* are not as blue and become green with age and the rhachis does not recurve as markedly or consistently.

3. The median leaflets of *Encephalartos horridus* are deeply lobed along the bottom margin and twist the leaflet out of plane, those of *E. trispinosus* are lobed only in the top third and are frequently much narrower and entire lower down on the leafstalk.

4. The cones of *Encephalartos horridus* are brownish-red over green, losing some of the brown hair at maturity, while those of *E. trispinosus* are golden-yellow with a wrinkled scale face.

*Hybrids of Encephalartos horridus:* This species grows together with *Encephalartos longifolius* at several localities and many hybrids have been observed. (Colour Plate 30, figs. 3 and 4.)

*Cultivation:* This a hardy and attractive species which responds well to cultivation. A well drained position in full sun is essential to preserve the blue colour of the leaves.

C. J. Chamberlin writing in 1919 said: 'Its terrible leaves give a clear title to its name . . . *Encephalartos horridus* is well named . . .'

# Plate 25. *Encephalartos trispinosus* (Hook) R. A. Dyer

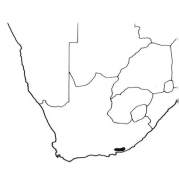

*Distribution:* EASTERN CAPE

*Encephalartos trispinosus* occurs in the lower reaches of the Bushman's River and the Great Fish River in the districts of Bathurst, Alexandria and Albany. Summer rainfall varies from 625 to 725 mm.

*Stem:* This is a low growing species and the stems seldom exceed 1 m with a diameter of 25 to 30 cm. Plants sucker freely from the base and large clusters are seen in the field.

*Leaves:* Considerable variation exists even in the same locality and *Encephalartos trispinosus* must be regarded as a very variable species. Typical forms have a leaf length of 0,75 to 1,25 m with the tip of the leaf slightly recurved. Leaf colour is also variable with glaucous blue leaves from the Fish River area while green leaved forms occur in the Bushman's River area. (See page 28 for a possible ecological explanation for this occurrence). The median leaflets are 10 to 18 cm long and 1,5 to 2,5 cm broad with one or two twisted lobes on the bottom margin. The leaflets along the lower third of the leafstalk are usually entire and much narrower.

*Cones:* This species has a solitary bright yellow cone. Male cones are 25 to 35 cm long and 7 to 8 cm in diameter. The female cones are 40 to 50 cm long and 18 to 20 cm in diameter. The female cone scales are deeply wrinkled.

*Seeds:* Reddish-orange coloured.

*Affinities:* A close relationship exists between *Encephalartos trispinosus* and *E. horridus*, in fact the former was classified under *E. horridus* until 1965. Prior to this, the species was known as *Encephalartos horridus* var. *trispinosus*. Although the leaves of this species are extremely variable the following features serve to distinguish it from *Encephalartos horridus*:

1. In *Encephalartos trispinosus* the leaflets of the lower third of the leaf are usually narrow and entire, while those of *E. horridus* are broad and lobed right to the base of the leafstalk.

2. The cones of *Encephalartos trispinosus* are bright yellow and the scale faces of the female cones are deeply wrinkled, the cones of *E. horridus* are brownish-red and the scale face is smooth.

*Hybrids:* Within the distribution area of *Encephalartos trispinosus*, two other species occur in close proximity and several hybrids have been recorded.

*E. trispinosus* × *E. altensteinii*

*E. trispinosus* × *E. arenarius*

Both the leaf and cone characters are variable and intermediate between the parent species. (See discussion under Hybridization, p. 39.)

*Cultivation:* This species is hardy and grows well in cultivation making new leaves and cones annually. It requires good drainage and a position in full sun.

The specific name '*trispinosus*' refers to the three spined lobes of the typical form.

## *Plate 25. E. trispinosus.* (Hook) R. A. Dyer

1
2

1. Leaf detail. Note that the leaflets are entire
   lower down.
2. Plant in habitat.
3. Male cone.
4. Female cone.

3
4

*Plate 26. E. ferox. Bertol. f.*

1. Male cones. Note that the cones are at various stages of maturity.
2. Female cone shedding seed.
3. Leaf detail.
4. Female cones.
5. Plant in habitat under an Umdoni tree *Syzygium cordatum*.

# Plate 26. *Encephalartos ferox* Bertol. f.

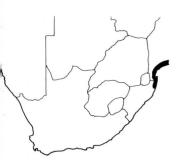

*Distribution:* NATAL and MOZAMBIQUE

*Encephalartos ferox* occurs in large numbers in the coastal bush of Zululand and northwards into Mozambique. It is usually found growing in the shade of the dune vegetation with its stems buried in the dune sand and leafmold. Rainfall varies from 1 000 to 1 250 mm per annum and no frost occurs.

*Stem:* This is a low growing species with stems seldom exceeding 1 m and with a diameter of 25 to 30 cm.

*Leaves:* The leaves are 1 to 2 m in length and a glossy dark green. The median leaflets are 15 cm long and 3,5 to 5 cm broad with 2 to 4 lobed teeth on both margins giving a ruffled hollylike shape to the leaf. The leaflets are closely spaced but in a horizontal plane to the rhachis making this a most attractive foliage species.

*Cones: Encephalartos ferox* bears a large number of cones, up to ten on male plants and as many as five on female plants. The cones are usually a brilliant scarlet, but golden-yellow ones occur in certain localities in Mozambique. Male cones are 40 to 50 cm long and 8 to 10 cm in diameter. Female cones are 25 to 50 cm in length and 20 to 40 cm in diameter.

*Seeds:* Dark glossy red.

*Affinities: Encephalartos ferox* is not closely allied to any of the other South African species and is easily identified by:

1. The glossy dark green leaflets with their marked pattern of teeth.
2. The bright red cones which are not found in any other species.

*Cultivation: Encephalartos ferox* is easily grown but requires some shade and copious amounts of water. Plants should be planted in a very sandy mixture with a good proportion of leafmold. If grown in dry inland areas in full sun, the leaves will burn and extremes of cold will likewise cause damage to the plant. Seedlings grow rapidly and records indicate that a plant of *Encephalartos ferox* produced its first cone after only twelve years.

The specific name '*ferox*' in botanical terms means '*strongly armed with teeth*'.

# Plate 27. *Encephalartos arenarius* R. A. Dyer

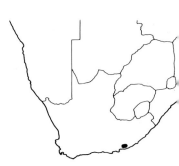

*Distribution:* EASTERN CAPE

*Encephalartos arenarius* occurs in the Alexandria district where it is found growing in the coastal sanddune forest in shade. The annual rainfall varies from 725 to 875 mm and no frost occurs.

*Stem:* Stems may be up to 1 m long, but the plants frequently appear to be subterranean as the stems are buried under the build up of sand and leafmold on the dunes. The diameter of the stem when exposed is 20 to 30 cm.

*Leaves:* The leaves are 1 to 1,5 m long and the rhachis recurves sharply at the tip. The leaf colour is mid-green with a distinct bloom. In some localities blue leafed forms occur but these are rare. The median leaflets are flat, 12 to 16 cm in length, 3 to 4 cm broad with three or four flat lobes.

*Cones:* The cones which are solitary are light green at maturity. Male cones are 30 to 50 cm long and 8 to 15 cm in diameter. Female cones are 50 to 60 cm long and 25 to 30 cm in diameter.

*Seeds:* Shiny red.

*Affinities: Encephalartos arenarius* is closely related to *E. latifrons*, but may be readily distinguished as follows:

1. *Encephalartos arenarius* is a medium sized plant which seldom exceeds 1 m while *E. latifrons* may have stems up to 3 m.

2. The leaf colour of *Encephalartos arenarius* is a medium green with a distinct bloom whereas the leaves of *E. latifrons* are a shiny dark green.

3. The median leaflets of *Encephalartos arenarius* although lobed, are not twisted out of the plane of the leaflet and are more widely spaced in the top third of the leaf than those of *E. latifrons* which so closely overlap upwards that they form a rigid interlocking pattern when viewed from the side. (Colour Plate 28, fig. 1.)

4. *Encephalartos arenarius* has a solitary light green cone with relatively smooth cone scales, those of *E. latifrons* are a deep olive-green with deeply wrinkled cone scales.

*Hybrids of Encephalartos arenarius:* A few plants have been recorded which points to hybridization between *Encephalartos arenarius* and *E. altensteinii*.

*Cultivation:* This species responds well to cultivation and should be grown in sand and leafmold with adequate moisture at all times. Two or even three whorls of leaves annually are not uncommon. This species is not frost hardy and should be grown in half shade to prevent the leaves burning in the full sun, particularly in areas where the humidity is low during summer.

The specific name '*arenarius*' means '*growing in sandy places*'.

*Plate 27. E. arenarius.* R. A. Dyer

1

2

1. Leaf detail.
2. Plant in habitat. Although this species usually
   grows in semi–shade under trees, this locality
   had been cleared for grazing.
3. Female cone.
4. Male cone.

3

4

# Plate 28. *E. latifrons*. Lehm.

1. Leaf detail. Note how the sharply lobed leaflets interlock to form a pattern.
2. Plant in habitat.
3. Male cones.
4. Female cone.

# Plate 28. *Encephalartos latifrons* Lehm.

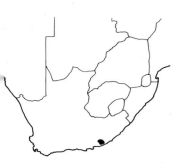

*Distribution:* EASTERN CAPE

*Encephalartos latifrons* occurs in scattered isolated groups on rocky outcrops among scrub bush in the Bathurst and Albany districts.

*Stem:* Stems may reach 3 m in height and the plants sucker freely from the base. Just prior to the new leaves emerging, the top of the stem and crown becomes very woolly.

*Leaves:* Leaves are 1 to 1,5 m in length, the top third of the rhachis recurves sharply with the tip curled back completely. The leaves are a dark glossy green with a clear, yellow rhachis. Median leaflets are 10 to 15 cm in length and 4 to 6 cm broad (excluding the lobes). The lower margin of the median leaflets has 3 to 4 triangular lobes which are twisted out of the plane of the leaflet. The leaflets closely overlap upwards in the top third of the leaf and viewed from the side, the lowest lobe points downwards, the top two lobes point upwards, thus creating an interlocking pattern.

*Cones:* 1 to 3 cones, dark olive-green in colour. The male cones are 30 to 50 cm long and 8 to 17 cm in diameter. Female cones are 50 to 60 cm long and 25 cm in diameter with the scale face deeply furrowed and wrinkled.

*Seeds:* Bright red.

*Affinities:* *Encephalartos latifrons* is closely related to *E. arenarius* and may be distinguished as follows:

1. *Encephalartos latifrons* is found only in inland districts as opposed to the coastal habitat of *E. arenarius* which occurs in the dune vegetation.

2. *Encephalartos latifrons* is a tall aborescent species with stems frequently reaching 3 m, while *E. arenarius* appears subterranean because the 1 m stems are often buried in the dune sand.

3. The dark shiny green leaflets of *Encephalartos latifrons* form a rigid interlocking pattern, while *E. arenarius* leaflets are a glaucous green with a bloom, and though lobed are widely spaced.

4. *Encephalartos latifrons* had 3 to 4 dark olive-green cones compared with the solitary light green cone of *E. arenarius*.

*Hybrids:* *Encephalartos latifrons* hybridises with *E. altensteinii* (see Colour Plate 30, fig. 2).

*Cultivation:* *Encephalartos latifrons* is an extremely rare, slow-growing species of which very few isolated clumps exist in the field. Due to its scattered distribution in nature (no male and female clumps are within pollinating distance of one another) active regeneration is not taking place and the species must therefore be considered in need of the most stringent protection. Recently, efforts by a dedicated conservationist has resulted in fertile hand-pollinated seed becoming available and it is hoped that this will re-establish the species in numbers and ensure its survival.

The specific name '*latifrons*' means '*broad leaves*' and with the exception of some forms of *Encephalartos ferox*, this species has the broadest leaves in the genus.

# Plate 29. *Stangeria eriopus* (Kunze) Nash

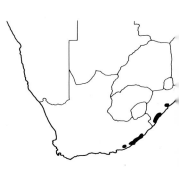

*Distribution:* EASTERN CAPE and NATAL

*Stangeria eriopus* occurs in coastal grassveld and inland forests in the districts of Bathurst, East London, Port St. Johns, Port Shepstone, Pinetown, Mtunzini, Eshowe and Ingwavuma.

*Stem:* Plants have a large tuberous root which is continuous with the main stem. The stem is subterranean and may be branched or unbranched. Occasionally the stem may branch into ten or twelve heads and each head may produce a cone at the same time.

*Leaves:* Up to four leaves grow from the top of the stem and these are very variable in size and shape depending on the habitat. In open grassland they may only be 25 to 30 cm in length while those growing under forest conditions may be 1 to 2 m tall. The size and the number of the leaflets also varies considerably. They may vary from 5 to 20 pairs and the lower ones have a short petiole while the upper ones are united with the rhachis. Median leaflets may be 10 to 40 cm in length and 2 to 6 cm broad. The leaflets have a prominent midvein. The margins of the leaves may be entire, serrated or deeply fringed according to the locality.

*Cones:* Each stem produces a solitary cone. Both male and female cones are silvery pubescent at first becoming brownish with age. Male cones are 10 to 15 cm in length and 3 to 5 cm in diameter with closely overlapping cone scales. The female cones are 18 to 20 cm in length and 8 to 10 cm in diameter. The scales of the female cone overlap closely.

*Seeds:* Red and almost round.

*Affinities:* At first glance the leaves of *Stangeria eriopus* resemble those of ferns and in fact it was first classified as *Lomaria eriopus*. Only when plants in cone were found, was it realised that it belonged to the broad cycad family. It is a monotypic genus in the family *Stangeriaceae*.

Various forms are found in different ecological habitats. Those growing in open grassland have short leaves with leaflets that are hard in texture and are rounded at the tips of the leaflets. The rootstock usually branches freely with each stem bearing a cone. Those growing under forest conditions have taller leaves (1 to 2 m) with numerous soft fringed leaflets. As there is no difference in the cones, separation into two different species does not appear to be justified.

*Cultivation:* *Stangeria eriopus* grows well under cultivation and responds to generous treatment. Ample moisture and light shade will produce luxuriant growth. Plants in the garden are frequently deciduous while those grown under greenhouse conditions may retain their leaves through two or three cycles. Plants are frost tender.

The name commemorates Dr William Stanger who became Surveyor General of Natal. The prefix 'erio-' means '*woolly*'.

*Plate 29. Stangeria eriopus.* (Kunze) Nash

1

2

1. Male cones.
2. Female cone.
3. Leaf detail. Note the prominent midvein.
4. Cone with seeds. The cone scales are not as
   fleshy as those of *Encephalartos* and by the time
   the seeds are mature, the cone scales have dried
   out and appear almost transparent.

3

4

Plate 30. Natural Hybrids and Intermediate Forms

# Plate 30. *Natural Hybrids and Intermediate Forms*

Fig. 1.

*E. altensteinii* x *E. villosus*

Hybrids show characters intermediate between those of the parent species. The leafstalk has prickles down to the base like *E. villosus* while the cone is tomentose at first and the cone scales have terminal facets similar to those of *E. altensteinii*. The cone scales of *E. villosus* overlap one another.

Fig. 2.

*E. altensteinii* x *E. latifrons*

Note the closely overlapping and crowded leaflets like those of *E. latifrons*. The leaflets are however not lobed like *E. latifrons* and are the bright green colour of *E. altensteinii* leaves.

Fig. 3.

*E. horridus* x *E. longifolius* (Female)

Characters nearer *E. horridus* are the marked lobes of the leaflets, and the structure and colour of the cone. The cone is yellowish-brown like that of *E. horridus* and has the same relatively smooth terminal facets to the cone scales. The colour of the leaves and the yellow rhachis are characters nearer to *E. longifolius*.

Fig. 4.

*E. horridus* x *E. longifolius* (Male)

The lobed leaflets and the rhachis which curls over are characters nearer to *E. horridus* as is the colour of the cone. The leaf colour and the fact that the lower leaflets are not lobed but entire are characters nearer to *E. longifolius*.

Fig. 5.

*E. umbeluziensis* x *E. villosus* (Female)

The leaves have prickles to the base like those of *E. villosus*. The cone is much larger than that of *E. umbeluziensis* and is the size, colour and shape of *E. villosus* cones. The structure of the cone scale is similar to that of *E. umbeluziensis* in the terminal facet which protrudes and is not fringed and overlapping as those of *E. villosus*.

Fig. 6.

*E. umbeluziensis* x *E. villosus* (Male)

The leaves are nearer to *E. umbeluziensis* but the cones though smaller and more slender are the colour and have the structure of those of *E. villosus*. *E. umbeluziensis* male cones are green at maturity with a marked terminal facet to the cone scale.

# Glossary

| | |
|---|---|
| *Adventitious roots* | A root which does not grow from the primary or lateral roots but from a leaf or stem. |
| *Angiosperms* | Plants that have their seeds enclosed in an ovary. |
| *Anorexy* | The lack of appetite. |
| *Apex* | The top portion of a leaf, or stem. |
| *Apogeotropic roots* | Roots which grow upwards to the surface of the soil, not downwards. |
| *Axis* | Botanically, the straight line of a plant about which the organs are arranged. |
| *Callus* | An abnormal thickening as at the base of a cutting. |
| *Cambium* | The layer of nascent tissue between the bark and the wood from which both are formed. |
| *Coralloid* | A coral-like mass. |
| *Cortex* | The outer layer of a tree. |
| *Cotyledons* | The seedleaves of the embryo plant. |
| *Cutinized* | The modification of the outer cells of a leaf so that they become impervious to liquids. |
| *Deciduous* | When the leaves of a plant die back or fall off in winter. |
| *Deflexed* | Curved downwards. |
| *Dehisce* | Splitting open of a seed or pollen sac when ripe. |
| *Dioecious* | When the male and female elements are found on separate plants. |
| *Ecotypes* | A plant which is modified by the ecology of its habitat. |
| *Endosperm* | The food-containing tissue of seeds. |
| *Entire* | A leaflet which has no teeth on its margins. |
| *Epidermis* | The outer layer or skin of the leaf. |
| *Epithet* | A descriptive phrase. |
| *Glaucous* | Dull green, bluish-green; covered with bloom. |
| *Gymnosperms* | Plants which bear seeds that are not enclosed in an ovary. |
| *Hypocotyledonary* | The area below the cotyledons and above the root. |
| *Hybrid* | A cross between two species of the same genus. |
| *Leaflet* | A unit of a compound leaf. |
| *Micropyle* | An opening in the skin of a seed – in cycads the opening which allows pollen to enter. |
| *Mutation* | A sudden change in the characteristics of the offspring which results in the formation of a new species. |
| *Nucellus* | The part of the ovule which contains the embryo sac. |
| *Ovipositor* | The egglaying organ of an insect. |
| *Ovule* | The unfertilized seed. |
| *Papillae* | Small raised protuberances. |
| *Petiole* | The stalk of a leaf. |
| *Proboscis* | The elongation of the nose. |
| *Procumbent* | Leaning and lying along the ground. |
| *Radicle* | A rudimentary root. |
| *Reflexed* | Curved backwards. |
| *Revolute* | Rolled back at the edge towards the underside. |
| *Rhachis* | The portion of a compound leaf above the petiole. |
| *Serrated* | With a notched edge like a saw. |
| *Stigma* | The part of the flower which receives the pollen. |
| *Stomata* | A breathing pore of a leaf. |
| *Style* | The part which lies between the ovary and the stigma. |
| *Symbiotic* | When two organisms depend for existence on one another. |
| *Tomentose* | Covered with woolly hairs. |
| *Transverse* | A cross cut through the longitudinal axis. |
| *Vascular* | Relating to the circulatory system. |
| *Whorls* | A ring of leaves. |
| *Xerophytic* | Relating to plants that can exist on a very small amount of moisture. |

# Index

Page numbers in italics denote the detailed description of the species, those in heavy type denote the coloured illustrations of the species.